English Song Book

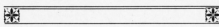

HARLEQUIN, SHEPPARD.

Frontispiece

English Song Book

COLLECTED AND EDITED
WITH AN INTRODUCTION

BY

HAROLD SCOTT

NEW YORK
ROBERT M. McBRIDE & COMPANY
1926

PRINTED IN GREAT BRITAIN.

PREFACE

HE history of Popular Songs in England is broken in many links—for much disturbance in the tradition has been caused by interpolations, in different cunning ways, of the Scientist Musician. Since the organised exploitation of popular music in the eighteenth century, one can usually trace the existence of a submerged, and often unconscious battle. On the one hand, the layman's demand for tune, pure and simple ; on the other the craftsman's efforts to wheedle the layman by devices other than the simple stimulus of race memory in music ; and to create a vogue, by an appeal to other instincts, such as voluptuousness, floridity, the dramatic contrast of soft and loud, or simply, in writing for singers by evoking admiration for physical endurance. This, though making no genuine or lasting appeal to the popular taste, secures for the craftsman the general acceptance of an individualised effort.

In making a collection of genuinely popular songs one is therefore less interested in the *tours de force* of fashionable musicianship, however successful at the time, than in the tunes through which one can trace an historical continuity. The genuine article is the song which can be sung and whistled without its harmonised accompaniment, and which refers itself back to a remote antiquity.

Early in the eighteenth century the veil was frankly lifted ; the moment had come for a reaction against the incursions of the Musician into the popular Theatre, and this gave Gay the opportunity of using for his lyrics the actual folk-songs and dances already known to the public through various instrumental arrangements. There already existed a famous collection of modern settings to traditional songs—" Pills to Purge Melancholy "—a final edition of which appeared in 1720. These and other collections were edited by Thomas D'Urfey, whose tremendous activity in the setting of old tunes—romantically heightened by his performance of them at the Court of three sovereigns —gives him the right of paternity in English Ballad Opera.

D'Ufrey almost happened on the " Beggar's Opera " in the course of his life-work, but never actually did. Gay stumbled on it, half-unconsciously, at the lucky moment: his idea had not been the founding of a popular native opera—as distinct from a merely native one which already existed—it had not even been primarily the burlesquing of Italian operatic methods ; so much as the simple notion of writing a " Newgate Pastoral." But the result was eagerly seized upon by the layman. The victory over composed music was thoroughly exploited, and the Musician for nearly forty years was elbowed from the operatic stage.

Although Gay's objective had been a literary one, the astounding success of the " Beggar's Opera " could not have been achieved without a remarkable musical sense. The selection of tunes used as settings to his brilliant verses reveals a complete mastery of his medium. It must have been a great joke for those of the audience who were in the know, to hear a country dance tune sung slowly, and with feeling, to the words " When the heart of a man is oppressed with care." But such subtleties as these were lost upon the crowd;

the work, in actual fact, popularised itself on the basis of a cheerful misunderstanding, and one reads of audiences being moved to tears by the pathos of the rendering of " Oh, ponder well, be not severe."

The tide having set that way, Ballad Opera met with no resistance until the 'sixties, when Arne produced his " Love in a Village."

The delusion that a musical movement was on foot was fostered everywhere. The patriotic note was struck in 1729 by Colley Cibber, rather redundantly. In the preface to his ballad opera, " Love in a Riddle," he referred to " the decay of English music owing to foreign influences " ; he complained about it in verse.

" Time was,"
he said,
> " e'en here when D'Urfey vamped a song,
> The same the courtier and the cobbler sung."

" Good songs,"
he protested,
> " will always candid hearers bring,
> Provided we find airs that they themselves may sing."

It was good for the public to feel that all the time they were having their ears tickled by traditional tunes they were supporting a movement in English Music, and there is no wonder that Ballad Opera held its own, though the highbrows were probably as dissatisfied with it all as they have recently been overjoyed with the revival of the " Beggar's Opera." But with the coming of Arne's " Love in a Village," a strange but inevitable thing happened. His brilliant compromise with Ballad Opera, a work without recitative, but including compositions from his own pen and those of some of his most brilliant contemporaries, was full of such compelling musical beauty that the Town was completely conquered, as it sometimes is by a good thing when it arrives at the right moment. Although, according to our definitions, a non-popular work, it carried the day, and established a new standard of high musical comedy. It is to be noted that the comic elements in the play are still treated traditionally, the comic song being the last to acquire a technique of its own.

The Music-hall had not yet been evolved from the taverns and drinking cellars. In addition to the Stage, the organised output of popular songs arrived by way of the Public Gardens, indoor assemblies such as the Pantheon, and Musical Societies such as the Catch Club (1761). Beside these there was the type of performance known as the Private Entertainment, popularised by Samuel Foote, and brilliantly developed by Charles Dibdin. The latter has some bearing on the evolution of the comic song, which was given individuality by his successors, among them Parry, who wrote "Wanted a Governess," and by John Braham. Dibdin's most celebrated sea-songs were first produced at Private Entertainments, and they had considerable popular influence.

The vogue for glees and catches reached its height, at this period, in the latter part of the century, but it was as a sporadic revival, destined to give way to other influences. The Musical Societies are important, however, in that they helped to preserve a popular musical tradition, and achieved a higher type of tavern entertainment which made the organised Victorian Music-hall a possibility. It was to glee parties and singers of part-songs that Morton turned when he founded his Music-hall at the Canterbury Arms in the 'sixties.

There remain the eighteenth century Pleasure Gardens, such as Vauxhall and Marylebone. The influence of these was spectacular, dramatic even—in the psychological sense, rather than musical. The creation of fantastic illusion rather than an every-day mass emotion, and the lack of intimacy inevitable in an open-air performance were antagonistic to purely popular music, and the catalogue of the Vauxhall concerts is an interminable list of florid arias.

It is absorbing to note the Age of Reason's excursions into the fantastic and one can scarcely exaggerate the significance of the aesthetic of such an essentially popular place as Vauxhall Gardens. Since it has become habitual to regard an aesthetic as incompatible with an actual mode of living, the groves, arcades and waterworks of Vauxhall—its fairy lamps, canals and leaden statuary have ceased to be taken seriously ; actually they were an expression of a deeply-rooted instinct which demands the creation of illusion in visible forms. That instinct suffered a chill in the political first days of the nineteenth century reducing even the Theatre, which fosters this instinct in its most concentrated form, to comparative impotence. In literature the objective, social-reformer imagination of Shelley was as inimical to it as the growth of commercialism to which it put up an enfeebled resistance. A romantic movement was actually on foot when Horace Walpole wrote his " Castle of Otranto," but this movement, which might have carried into English literature a dramatised conception of imaginative life, unfortunately ended with Beckford and Monk Lewes, although the genius of Keats and Coleridge is really a marvellous late flowering of the same impulse.

To return to the Stage. The introduction of Pantomime provided an important vehicle for popular songs ; its origins, however, are slightly confused. Chambers' Dictionary, under the heading of Pantomime, speaks of it as the attempt to create a "popular representation" out of the "so-called English Opera of the 17th Century," qualifying this by stating that the tendency has since become to produce a merely spectacular entertainment as an appendage to the Italian Opera. It then quotes Thurmond's "Dr. Faustus" (1729) as the first English effort in pure Pantomime ; a production in which the character of Faust merges itself with the Mask of Harlequin, and which introduces characters from the Italian Comedy of Art. This statement points to the entanglement of a number of forms. The seventeenth century Opera may be divided into the more operatic forms of Masque, influenced by the Italian Pastoral, and the pure operatic form which Purcell inherited from Byrd. To the former we can ascribe the taste for spectacular device which characterised the growth of Pantomime from its beginnings, as a piece of action with musical accompaniment. The new entertainment popularised by Thurmond was, therefore, a comic action embodying the characters of the Italian Comedy, and concluding in the manner of a classic masque.

The importance of Thurmond's work and his predecessors lay in the popular character of the fusion he adopted (comic miming, dancing, spectacular devices, music), and the natural addition of songs and dialogues (the "new speaking Pantomime") was finally the means

To face p. xi.

CREMORNE GARDENS IN 1858

of introducing all the other forms of theatrical entertainments which served as a vehicle for popular songs on the stage. Although bearing different names, such as Burletta or Extravaganza, these variants are often only slightly distinguishable from one another. The Harlequinade, as it has till recently survived, is of course the more or less unadulterated residuum of Thurmond's original scheme.

The introduction of "speaking Pantomime" was the opening of the flood-gate which leads us to the great singing clowns of the early nineteenth century, headed by Grimaldi, and by way of them to comedians such as Robson and Sam Cowell who, like Grimaldi, still held the stage, not only as comic vocalists, but as actors with a repertory of comic songs. The transference of these comedians and their immediate successors to the newly-reorganised tavern concert founded the modern, but already defunct music-hall comedian.

The Public Gardens were now decadent. Vauxhall, which trickled on into the 'thirties, was not replaced by any other garden of first importance, although before its death "Baron" Beaufain had opened his grounds in Chelsea for the "Tuition and practice of skilful and manly exercises." This was destined to become the well-known Cremorne of the 'fifties, and its leap into fame synchronised with the founding of the Canterbury Arms. Morton's original conception was rigidly respectable : a concert with glee singing, not even avoiding the great masters, but given under sociable conditions. But matters soon adjusted themselves ; the comic singers, headed by Cowell, were invited to take part ; the serious choral singing was dropped out (one could hear that kind of thing under

Sir William Sterndale-Bennett's baton at the Crystal Palace), and the Canterbury Arms set a new note in entertainment which the humbler tavern sing-songs were not slow to emulate. A new race of music-hall comedians sprang up, highly specialised, with far less general culture than the actor-vocalists who had preceded them, but whose rendering of the now completely evolved comic song established a vigorous hold on the public, and, at a later date, made illustrious the names of such men as G. H. Macdermott, George Leybourne and the " Great " Vance. The day of the comedienne also dawned ; she specialised at first in a rather coyer type of song, " The Captain and his Whiskers," " Be quiet, I will call my mother," and the publishers eagerly produced edited versions to which they gave the disarming title of " Ladies' Comic Songs."

An important development in the Victorian music-hall was the introduction into England, on the wave of slave liberation sentiment, of the nigger or pseudo-nigger troupes. The first of these, under the title of the " Ethiopian Serenaders," appeared in the 'forties ; they brought with them songs only faintly coloured by actual negroid characteristics, and without a semblance of syncopated rhythm. There were one or two good songs such as "Jump Jim Crow," " The Boatman's Dance," and " Nelly Bly," but they presented an almost Victorianised nigger, affected by all the sentimental obsessions of the period—temperance, the nemesis of conjugal infidelity, and filial reverence.

A long process of reproducing these sentimental pieties in the crudest form gives the repertory of the " Christy Minstrels " a compact sociological interest.

Preface

Even as early as the work of Charles Dibdin a weakening of the subject-matter and a tendency to conventionalise sentiment is apparent. In the work of Reeve, Haynes Bailey, Bishop, Alexander Lee and others, the tendency is completed, and the " Boudoir Ballad " fairly launched. The phrase was chosen by Bailey, for his album of songs issued in 1830, of which " We met, 'twas in a crowd " became the most famous. A tremendous outpouring of this type of song succeeded, and incredibly prolific writers—John Bennett, Blockley, Henry Russell, and others— swamped the market with them. It is not without significance that they often searched for subject matter in a purely conventional treatment of social questions ; their songs often suggest a faint reflection of the Dickensian " social purpose," which transcended, but was closely related to a tendency of the time ; a tendency towards the politer forms of intellectual curiosity. Occasionally one meets with an author with a touch of strength or sincerity, such as Henry Russell—the most prolific of them all—one or two of whose songs ring true.

But these were not the most fundamental sources of popular song in the Victorian period ; for these sources we must turn to the public-house, or at least to the saloon attached to it, and subsequently to the music-hall ; for although even at the outset a specialised article, the music-hall song has the true note of tradition, and the rise, in an incredibly short space of time, of the enormously popular comic and serio-comic vocalists shows how quickly an organic instinct can re-assert itself.

By the 'fifties the popular influence of the Saloon concerts had been fully established, and of these the most central and the most notorious was Evans's Song and Supper Rooms. Evans's, as it existed in 1851, provided an English variant of the Cafe-concert, completely suited to the bohemian taste of the time. Thackary's "Cave of Harmony" is a composite picture of this and of the smaller Supper Rooms in the Strand. At 1 a.m. the place was in full swing ; at the long supper tables ranks of cigar-smoking men were to be seen eating oysters and poached eggs on steak ; they sat in a large hall, splendidly gilt, with a curtained stage, embellished with the "grand piano-forte de rigeur," and with a ladies' gallery above divided into little private boxes.

The rapid celebrity of the Song and Supper Rooms, and the tendency to put emphasis on indoor performances at popular resorts were the steps by which the latter specialised entertainment was achieved. The Canterbury Arms concerts which became the Canterbury Music-Hall, have already been touched on ; the metamorphosis was effected by one Morton, and his success was established primarily by the comic singing of Sam Cowell : this happened in the 'sixties.

Although perhaps the most famous, Morton's Music-hall was by no means the first of its kind ; the Standard in Pimlico, which is now the Victoria Palace, held an older licence. But the Canterbury Music-hall established the type, as distinct from the earlier Saloon Theatre, and severed alliance with the Pleasure Gardens. Numerous halls, all outgrowths from a tavern centre, followed quickly on the Canterbury, and in all these houses the "lion comique" was the principal factor in establishing their reputation. The Music-hall sprang up from new groupings of men,—a new gesture in entertainment was in the making, involving a far more specialised and narrowly-defined technique ; the older Saloons and Pleasure Gardens, among them the famous " Grecian," gradually dropped out without achieving the transition.

The Grecian Saloon had been the most famous of the resorts east of the Mansion House ; it was in the City Road, and allied to the Eagle Tavern—a unit in the typical combination of public-house, pleasure garden and theatre. Famous early in the century as a miniature Vauxhall, with a complete equipment—cosmoramas, Chinese lanterns, statues, pavilions and dripping rocks—the proprietor in 1837 had sought further to cast a romantic glamour over the place, by purchasing and setting up at the entrance to the Gardens the actual triumphal decorations placed in front of Westminster Abbey for Queen Victoria's coronation. The Grecian had had a varied history ; it was celebrated for the acting and comic singing of Robson, the creator of " Villikins " ; opera-bouffe, ballet and pantomime had been performed there—especially the latter—and, in 1851, performances of a " Midsummer Night's Dream," preceded by a lecture by E. L. Blanchard, had been given,—a form of enter-tainment which has been perpetuated by Miss Baylis at the " Old Vic." It is difficult to comprehend that this programme should have formed a realistic policy in the theatre, but it was so, and one can judge the vigour of the transition period by the fact that the songs of " Jolly John Nash " were alternated at the Strand Music-Hall with performances of the Masque of Comus. Specialisation is the key-note from Morton onwards, before then a catholicity which would seem astonishing to us now.

CONTENTS

XVIII CENTURY SONGS

B

CONTENTS (cont.)—XIX Century Songs

*Reproduced by kind permission of Messrs. Edwin Ashdown, Ltd., 19, Hanover Square, W. 1.

†Reproduced by kind permission of Messrs. Ascherberg, Hopwood and Crew, Ltd., 16, Mortimer Street, W. 1.

‡Reproduced by kind permission of The Herman Darewski Music Publishing Co., 6, New Compton Street, W.C. 2.

ESSEX HARMONY.

—— *Being a Choice* ——

COLLECTION

of the most Celebrated

SONGS, CATCHES, CANONS.

EPIGRAMS, CANZONETS, and GLEES.

—— *For* ——

Two, Three, Four, Five, and Nine Voices,

From the Works of the

Most Eminent Masters.

Pr. 5ˢ·

LONDON.

Printed & Sold at Bland & Weller's, Music Warehouse, 23, Oxford Strᵗ·

A MEETING OF THE CATCH CLUB

To face p. 1.

Eighteenth Century Songs

THERE WAS AN OLD WOMAN

THE WATCHMAN'S SONG

THERE WAS AN OLD WOMAN

From " The Jovial Crew."

T HERE was a maid went to the Mill,
    Sing trolly lolly, lolly, lolly lo ;
The Miller turned round, but the Maid stood still,
    Oh oh ho, oh oh ho, oh oh ho, did she so ?

The Miller kissed her—away she went,
    Sing trolly lolly, lolly, lolly lo,
The Maid was well pleased and the Miller content,
    Oh oh ho, oh oh ho, oh oh ho, was it so ?

He danced and he sung while the mill went clack,
    Sing trolly lolly, lolly, lolly lo,
And he cherished his heart with a cup of old sack—
    Oh oh ho, oh oh ho, oh oh ho, did he so ?

THE WATCHMAN'S SONG

Charles Dibdin.   From the " Touchstone."

M Y name's Ted Blarney I'll be bound—
    Man and boy upon this ground
Full twenty years I've beat my round,
    Crying Vauxhall Watch !

THE WATCHMAN'S SONG.—A song in a pantomime by the celebrated
Charles Dibdin. Dibdin's work covered a large field. He started life as
an actor-vocalist, and, as a composer, made his name in Ballad Opera.
Most of the music of " Lionel and Clarissa " is by him. His contribution to
the later fully-fledged comic opera included " The Waterman " and " The
Quaker " ; he also wrote music to Fielding's wonderful burlesque, " Tom
Thumb," presumably from Knoe O'Hara's arrangements. His most in-
dividual achievement was the Private Entertainment ; this was a kind of
one-man revue which he carried on for many years and for which he wrote
innumerable songs, including " Tom Bowling " and the sea-songs.

SWEET WILLIAM'S FAREWELL TO BLACK-EYED SUSAN

SWEET WILLIAM'S FAREWELL TO BLACK-EYED
SUSAN

Richard Leveridge.   Words by John Gay.

ALL in the Downs the Fleet was moor'd,
    The streamers waving in the wind,
When Black-eyed Susan came on board
    " O where shall I my true love find ?
Tell me, jovial sailors, tell me true,
If my Sweet William sails among the crew ? "

William, who high upon the yard
    Rocked with the billows to and fro,
Soon as her well-known voice was heard
    He sighed and cast his eyes below ;
The cord slides swiftly through his glowing hands
And quick as lightning on the deck he stands.

O Susan, Susan, lovely dear,
    My vows shall ever true remain,
Let me kiss off that falling tear ;
    We only part to meet again.
Change as ye list, ye winds ; my heart shall be
The faithful compass that still points to thee.

Believe not what the landsmen say
    Who tempt with doubts thy constant mind ;
They'll tell, the sailors when away
    In ev'ry port a mistree find ;
Yes, yes, believe them when they tell thee so,
For thou art present everywhere I go.

The Boatswain gave the dreadful word,
    The sails their swelling bosoms spread,
No longer must she stay aboard,
    They kissed ; she sighed, he hung his head.
" Adieu," she cries, and waved her lily hand.

SWEET WILLIAM'S FAREWELL TO BLACK-EYED SUSAN.—
Richard Leveridge was an actor-vocalist, a conservative and stereotyped
performer. He had a rich bass voice, and was in the habit of challenging
people to singing contests. Usually a dull composer, he had the luck to set
this lyric of Gay's, and to strike a rich popular vein in his song " The Roast
Beef of Old England." Gay's lyric, (which was published as a separate
song) belongs to February, 1733.

LILLIBULERO

LILLIBULERO

H O Brother Teaghe, dost hear de decree ?
    Lillibulero, bullen a la,
Dat we shall have a new Deputie.
    Lillibulero, bullen a la
    Lero, lero, Lillibulero,
    Lillibulero, bullen a la
    Lero, lero, lillibulero
    Lillibulero, bullen a la.

Ho ! by my shoul it is de Talbot,
And he will cut all de English throat.

Tho' by my shoul de English do praat
De Law'n on dare side and Creist knows what.

But, if dispence do come from de Pope,
We'll hang Magna Charta and demselves in a rope.

And de good Talbot is made a Lord,
And he with brave lads is coming aboard.

Who all in France have taken a sware
Dat dey will have no Protestant heir.

O, but why does he stay behind ?
Ho ! By my shoul 'tis a Protestant wind.

Now Tyrconnel is come ashore,
And we shall have Commissioners gilore.

And he dat will not go to Mass
Shall turn out and look like an ass.

Now, now de hereticks all go down
By Creist and St. Patrick, de Nation's our own.

"Was written, or at least republished, on the Earl of Tyrconnel's going a
second time to Ireland in 1688 . . . Lill. and Bull. are said to have been
words of distinction used among the Irish Papists in their massacre of
Protestants, in 1641."—Chappell.
The Tune is a harpsichord lesson, by Henry Purcell.

BRIGHTON CAMP

BRIGHTON CAMP

I 'M lonesome since I crossed the hill,
    And o'er the moor and valley,
Such heavy thought my heart do fill
    Since parting with my Sally.
I seek no more the fine and gay,
    For each does but remind me
How swift the hours did pass away
    With the girl I left behind me,
    With the girl I left behind me.

Had I the art to sing her praise
    With all the skill of Homer,
One only theme should fill my lays,
    The charm of my true lover.
So let the night be e'er so dark,
    Or e'er so wet and windy,
Kind heaven send me back again
    To the girl I left behind me,
    To the girl I left behind me.

Her golden hair, in ringlets fair,
    Her eyes like diamonds shining,
Her slender waist, with carriage chaste,
    They leave the swan repining.
Ye gods alone ! oh, hear my prayer,
    To my beauteous fair to bind me,
And send me safely back again
    To the girl I left behind me,
    To the girl I left behind me.

The bee shall honey taste no more,
    The dove become a ranger,
The falling waves shall cease to roar
    E'er I shall seek to change her.
The vows we register'd above
    Shall ever cheer and bind me
In constancy to her I love—
    The girl I left behind me.
    The girl I left behind me.

WHAT THO' I AM A COUNTRY LASS

OLD KING COLE

WHAT THO' I AM A COUNTRY LASS

Charles Coffey.   From " The Devil to Pay."

IN plain stuff gown, an short-ear'd coif,
    Hard Labour did endure—a
Tho' late I was a cobbler's wife
    In cottage most obscure—a.

The scene is chang'd, I've altered quite,
    And from poor humble Nell—a
I'll learn to dance, to read and write,
    And from all bear the Bell—a.

WHAT THO' I AM A COUNTRY LASS.—This is the name given by
Charles Coffey to a version of the tune to which Carey's " Sally in our Alley "
came to be sung.

OLD KING COLE

From " Achilles."   By John Gay

NO more be Coy, give a loose to Joy,
    And let Love for thy pardon sue.
A glance could all my rage destroy
    And light up my Flame anew.
For tho' no man can stand at bay
    Against a Woman's Will,
And keep amid the loudest fray
    His Resolution still :
Yet when consenting smile accost
The man in her arms is lost.

OLD KING COLE.—Gay wrote " Achilles " as a burlesque on the neo-
classical tragedies of the time. As always, the audience missed the point,
and the play failed, although in the prologue he has been careful to say
    " My scene now shows the heroes of old Greece,
    But how, 'tis monstrous ! in a comick piece."
Gay wrote this work just after he had lost his fortune in the South Sea Bubble.
It was performed posthumously.

BUTTER'D PEASE

FIE ! NOW PRITHEE JOHN.

BUTTER'D PEASE

By John Gay.   From " Achilles."

SHOULD the Beast of the noblest race
　　Act the Brute of the lowest class ;
Tell me which do you think most base,
　　Or the Lion or the Ass ?

Boast not then of thy Rank or State ;
　　That but shows thee the meaner Slave.
Take thy due then of Scorn and Hate,
　　As thou'rt but the greater Knave.

FIE ! NOW PRITHEE JOHN.

Charles Coffey.   From " The Devil to Pay."

'TIS I vow and swear very cruel, dear,
　　Not to be allowed to talk :
Hence I say get in to thy wheel and spin,
　　Lest up on your back my strap should walk.
Well since I must I will be gone,
Go, go you are a naughty man ;
Be sure get drunk then, if you can
　　Reel home to Nell.

You surly jade, by Yea and Nay,
If here you any longer stay
Or dare dispute my sovereign sway,
　　I'll strap you well.

FIE ! NOW PRITHEE JOHN.—A paraphrase of a well-known catch.

LEATHER APRON

THE BUDGEON IS A FINE TRADE

LEATHER APRON

Charles Coffey, 1748.   From " The Devil to Pay."

OF all the plagues of human life
    A shrew is sure the worst ;
Scarce one in ten who takes a wife
    But with a shrew is cursed.

Since then, the plague in marriage lies,
    Who'd rush upon his fate?
When he for freedom, bondage buys,
    And still repents too late.

THE BUDGEON IS A FINE TRADE

Words by Charles Coffey.   From " The Devil to Pay."

THO' ravished from my husband's arms,
    To dwell in stench and pain,
I'll break thro' all their Majick charms
    And liberty regain.
Then sweet Revenge shall calm my woes,
    And every grief asswage ;
Whilst all who did my bliss oppose
    Shall feel my powerful rage.

THE BUDGEON IS A FINE TRADE.—This tune is the " Jolly Miller "
quoted by Bickerstaffe in " Love in a Village." It is interesting to notice
how a cheerful song like " The Miller of the Dee " which this most usually is,
can take on such an obligingly tragic ring under the persuasion of Mr. Coffey.

c

ONE EVENING

CATCH

ONE EVENING

From " The Jovial Crew."

FAIR maidens, O ! beware
Of using men too well,
Their pride is all their care,
They only kiss to tell.

How hard the Virgin's fate !
While every way undone ;
The Coy grow out of date,
They're ruined if they're won . . .

CATCH

By White.

NEW oysters, new oysters, new oysters, new,
Have you any wood to cleave ?
Have you any wood to cleave ?
Have you any wood to cleave ?
What kitchen stuff have you, maids ?
What kitchen stuff have you, maids ?

NEW OYSTERS.—One of many catches based on street cries. A catch
in the same volume has the following note appended to it : " The first part
is, in many places in England, the well-known cry of a certain limping
ink-seller."

CATCH

CATCH

CATCH

By J. F. Lampe.   From The Catch Club Collection.

HOT mutton pyes, hot !
    Buy my dainty young beans, my young beans !
Crabs, crabs, any crabs.

CATCH

By Henry Purcell.   From The Catch Club Collection.

I GAVE her cakes ; I gave her ale,
    I gave her sack and sherry ;
I kist her once, I kist her twice,
    And we were wondrous merry.

I gave her beads and bracelets fine,
    And I gave her gold down derry,
I thought she was afear'd till she stroked my beard,
    And we were wondrous merry.

Merry my heart, merry my cocks, merry my sprights,
    Merry my hey down derry,
I kist her once and I kist her twice,
    And we were wondrous merry.

QUOTH ROGER TO NELLY

QUOTH ROGER TO NELLY

By Richard Woodward, Junr.   From " The Essex Harmony."

QUOTH Roger to Nelly, suppose I were dead,
　Suppose I were dead, quoth Roger to Nelly,
Suppose I were dead, would you get another,
Would you get another good man in my stead ?　In my stead ?
　　　In my stead ?
Would you get you another good man in my stead ?

Yes that I would, Roger, Oh Roger, Oh Roger,
Pray man, do not stare, do not stare, do not stare,
Yes that I would, Roger, Oh Roger, Oh Roger,
Pray, man, do not stare, do not stare, do not stare,
Would you have me hug pillow and bolster, my dear ?
Would you have me hug pillow and bolster, my dear ?
　　　And bolster, my dear ?

ADAM CATCHED EVE

THE AMOUROUS PARTY

ADAM CATCHED EVE

By J. Baildon.   From " The Essex Harmony."

A DAM catched Eve by the furbelow,
   Adam catched Eve by the furbelow,
And that's the oldest catch I know,
And that's the oldest catch I know,
And that's the oldest catch I know,
Oh ho ! did he so, did he so, did he so,
Did he so, did he so, did he so ?

THE AMOUROUS PARTY

Edward Mulso.   From " The Essex Harmony."

D ON'T push, don't push, don't push,
   Don't push my tender passion ;
You hurt, you hurt, you hurt,
   You hurt my reputation.
Go no further I'll cry murther,
Go no further I'll cry murther,
Lie still, lie still, lie still,
   Lie still, fond inclination.

THE AMOUROUS PARTY.—One of the catches from the " Essex Harmony." It is a discreet instance of a type of catch then much in vogue, which can hardly be quoted to-day.

ON A DRAM

ON A DRAM

By J. Baildon.

WHEN is it best, said John to Joan ;
　　When is it best, when is it best, when is it best,
Said John to Joan,
When is it best, when is it best, when is it best,
Said John to Joan,
At night, at morning or at noon,
At night, at morning, or at noon,
At morning or at noon, at night,
At morning or at noon, at night,
At morning, at noon, at noon, at night.
At morning, or at noon.　Why ?

Faith, quoth Joan, to tell thee right,
I like it noon and night and night,
I like it noon, I like it night,
I like it morning, noon and night,
I like it morning, noon and night,
To tell thee right, to tell thee right,
I like it morning, noon and night.
I like it morning, I like it noon,
I like it morning, noon and night and night,
Why, faith, quoth Joan, to tell thee right,
Why, faith, quoth Joan, to tell thee right,
I like it morning, noon, and night.

ON A DRAM.—This catch is given as an instance of the complicated technique in this form of writing.　It won the prize medal offered by the Catch Club in 1763.

THREE OXFORD CRIES

EPITAPH

THREE OXFORD CRIES

Dr. Hayes.

CHAIRS to mend, old chairs to mend,
    Rush or cane-bottomed old chairs to mend,
Old chairs to mend, old chairs to mend.

New mackerel, new mackerel, new mackerel, new mackerel ;
Old rags, any old rags, take money for your old rags ;
Any hare skins or rabbit skins.

EPITAPH

WIND, gentle evergreens, to form a shade,
    Around the tomb, where Sophocles is laid ;
Sweet Ivy lend thine aid, and intertwine
With blushing roses and the clust'ring vine.
So shall thy lasting leaves with beauty hung,
Prove grateful emblems of the lays he sung.

JOAN'S PLACKET IS TORN

SINCE HODGE PROVES UNGRATEFUL

JOAN'S PLACKET IS TORN

From " Love in a Village," by Isaac Bickerstaffe.

WHEN I followed a lass who was froward and shy,
   I stuck to her, stuff
Till I made her comply.
I took her so lovingly round the waist,
And hugged her tight and held her fast ;
   When hugged and hauled,
   She screamed and squalled.
But, tho' she vowed all that I did was in vain,
I pleased her so well, that she bore it again.
I pleased her so well, that she bore it again.
   Hoighty toity, whisking frisking,
   Green was her gown upon the grass,
Oh, those were the joys of our dancing days,
Oh, those were the joys of our dancing days.

JOAN'S PLACKET IS TORN.—A variant of this tune is supposed to have been used as a Fanfare at the execution of Mary, Queen of Scots. The above words were stolen by Isaac Bickerstaffe, from Colley Cibber's " Love in a Riddle."

SINCE HODGE PROVES UNGRATEFUL

Music by Arne.   From " Love in a Village."

SINCE Hodge proves ungrateful, no further I'll seek,
   But go up to town, in a wagon next week.
Service in London is no such disgrace,
And Register's office will get me a place.
Bet Blossom went there, and soon met with a friend,
They say, that in silks she's now standing an end.
Then why should I not the same maxim pursue,
And better my fortune as other girls do ?
And better my fortune as other girls do.

GENTLE YOUTH—AH, TELL ME WHY

STILL IN HOPE TO GET THE BETTER

GENTLE YOUTH—AH, TELL ME WHY

Music by Arne. From " Love in a Village."

GENTLE Youth—Ah ! tell me why
Still you force me thus to fly,
Cease, Oh cease to persevere,
Speak not what I must not hear.
To my heart its ease restore,
Go, and never see me more.
To my heart its ease restore.

STILL IN HOPE TO GET THE BETTER

Music by Arne. From " Love in a Village."

STILL in hope to get the better
Of my stubborn Flame I try,
Of my stubborn Flame I try.
Swear this moment to forget her
And the next, my oath deny.
And the next, my oath deny.

Now prepared with scorn to treat her,
Every charm in thought I brave,
Every charm in thought I brave.
Then relapsing, fly to meet her,
And confess myself her slave.
And confess myself her slave.

D

ROSETTA'S SONG

HOUSEMAID'S SONG

ROSETTA'S SONG

Music by Arne.   In Act I of "Love in a Village."

MY heart's my own, my will is free,
    And so shall be my voice,
No mortal man shall wed with me
    Till first he's made my choice.
Let parents rule by Nature's hand,
    And children still obey,
And is there then no saving clause
    Against tyrannic sway ?
    Against tyrannic sway ?
And is there then no saving clause
    Against tyrannic sway ?

HOUSEMAID'S SONG

Tune of Nancy Dawson.   From "Love in a Village."

I PRAY you gently list to me,
    I'm young and strong and clean to see ;
I'll not turn tail to any she
For work that's in the country.

Of all your house the charge I take,
I wash, I scrub, I brew, I bake,
And more can do than here I'll speak,
Depending on your bounty.

OH HAD I BEEN BY FATE DECREED

LET GAY ONES AND GREAT

OH HAD I BEEN BY FATE DECREED

Music by Dr. Howard.   " Young Meadows' " song from " Love in a Village."

OH, had I been by Fate decreed
  Some humble cottage swain,
In fair Rosetta's sight to feed
  My flocks upon the plain.
In fair Rosetta's sight to feed
  My flocks upon the plain.

What joys I had been born to taste
  Which now I ne'er must know ?
Ye envious Pow'rs ! why have ye placed
  My Fair One's lot so low ?
Ye envious Pow'rs ! why have ye placed
  My Fair One's lot so low ?

LET GAY ONES AND GREAT

Music by J. Baildon.   From " Love in a Village."

LET gay ones and great
  Make the most of their fate,
  From pleasure to pleasure they run ;
  From pleasure to pleasure they run ;
Well, who cares a jot,
I envy them not,
  While I have my dog and my gun.
  While I have my dog and my gun.

O'ONS ! NEIGHBOURS NE'ER BLUSH

SALLY IN OUR ALLEY

O'ONS ! NEIGHBOURS NE'ER BLUSH

Arne.   From " Love in a Village."

O'ONS ! Neighbours ne'er blush
   For a trifle like this.
What harm, with a fair one,
   To toy and to kiss ?

The greatest of greatest
   (A truce with grimace)
Would do the same thing
   Were they in the same place.

No Age, no Profession,
   No Station is free,
To Sovereign Beauty
   Mankind bend the knee.

That Power resistless
   No strength can oppose,
We all love a pretty girl
   Under the rose,

   Under the rose,
   Under the rose,
We all love a pretty girl,
   Under the rose.

SALLY IN OUR ALLEY

Henry Carey.

BUT of all ye songsters in ye land
   There's none like Faranelli,
He'll make your heart to jump and start,
   And caper in your belly.

Young men of Arts may bray of parts,
   They're all a pack of ninnies,
He shows most sense who gets most sense,
   And pockets all the guineas.

SALLY IN OUR ALLEY.—This burlesqued version of Carey's famous song was written by the author himself, and introduced into his " Musical Hodge-Podge."

GOOD MORROW, GOSSIP JOAN

THO' YOU BY CONSTRAINT

GOOD MORROW, GOSSIP JOAN

WHY how now, Madam Flirt,
    If you thus must chatter,
And are for flinging dirt,
    Let's see who best can spatter.
      Madam Flirt !
Why how now, saucy jade,
    Sure the wench is tipsy !
How can you see me made
    The scoff of such a gipsy ?
      Saucy Jade !

THO' YOU BY CONSTRAINT

By Charles Coffey.   From " The Boarding School."

WHEN Teachers are all fast asleep,
    I'll steal out by telling some fib,
Then to my true love I'll creep
    And a fig for my apron and bib !

Mamma shan't a fool make of me,
    Too old to be whipt I am grown,
For a baby no longer I'll be,
    But a baby I'll have of my own.

THE BOARDING SCHOOL.—Coffey wrote " The Boarding School " in 1733 ; it was cribbed from a comedy called " Love for Money " by Tom D'Urfey. Charles Coffey's work is brilliant, and distinctly sadistic in tone: cf. songs in " The Devil to Pay." He edited a collection of Drayton's poems, and had literary connections with John Mottley (with whom he wrote " The Devil to Pay "), and Thomas, known as Hesiod, Cook, who wrote " learned farces " adapted from Terence. Coffey was also an actor, and played the part of "Aesop" in Dublin.

THUS FIDDLERS AND ARCHERS

FROM THE BOARDING SCHOOL

THUS FIDDLERS AND ARCHERS

By Charles Coffey.   From " The Boarding School."

WHEN maids to the joys of soft love do incline,
    What force can restrain their desire ?
Charms to the youthful and gay they resign,
And from withered age still retire,
And from withered age still retire.

FROM THE BOARDING SCHOOL

Charles Coffey.

SHE, she alone has ev'ry charm
    Which can at once or cure or kill,
Her eyes the coldest heart can warm
    And draw the hermit from his cell.
Beauty and Virtue round her shine,
Oh ! that the powers would make her mine !

FROM THE BOARDING SCHOOL.—The same words as the above are
to be found to a different version of the tune in the 1719 edition of " Pills to
Purge Melancholy."

OH DEAR! WHAT CAN THE MATTER BE?

JACK RATLIN

OH DEAR! WHAT CAN THE MATTER BE?

OH Dear ! What can the matter be ?
    Oh Dear ! What can the matter be ?
Oh Dear ? What can the matter be ?
Johnny's so long at the Fair.
He promised he'd bring me a basket of posies,
A garland of lilies, a garland of roses,
A little straw hat to set off the blue ribbons
    That tie up my bonny brown hair.

OH DEAR! WHAT CAN THE MATTER BE.—The first published
record of this song is in the British Lyre for 1792. It was sung as a favourite
duet at " Harrison's Concerts." Samuel Harrison was a singer who married
a soprano with the appropriate name of Miss Cantelo ; he performed at the
first of the concerts of Ancient Music in 1776.

JACK RATLIN

From " Liberty Hall," by Charles Dibdin.

JACK RATLIN was the ablest seaman
    None like him could hand reef or steer,
No dangerous toil but he'd encounter
    With skill, and in contempt of fear.
In fight a lion, the battle ended
    Meek as the bleating lamb he'd prove,
Thus Jack had courage, manners, merit,
    Yet did he sigh and all for love.

The song, the jest, the flowing liquor,
    For none of these had Jack regard,
The while his messmates were carousing,
    High sitting on the pendant yard,
Would think upon his fair one's beauties,
    Swear never from such charms to rove,
That truly he'd adore them living
    And, dying, sigh—to end his love.

The same express, the Crew commanded
    Once more to view their native land
Amongst the rest, brought Jack some tidings
    Would it have been his fair one's hand.
Oh Fate ! her death deplored the letter,
    Instant his pulse forgot to move,
With quivering lips and eyes uplifted
    He heav'd a sigh and died for love.

THE HIGH-METTLED RACER

THE HIGH-METTLED RACER

From " Liberty Hall."   Charles Dibdin.

SEE the course throng'd with gazers, the sports are begun,
The confusion, but hear I'll bet you, Sir, done done !
Ten thousand strange murmurs resound far and near ;
Lords, hawkers and jockeys assail the tir'd ear,
Lords, hawkers and jockeys assail the tir'd ear.

While with neck like a rainbow erecting his crest,
Pampered, prancing and pleased, his head touching his breast,
Scarcely snuffing the air, he's so proud and elate,
The high-mettled racer first starts for the plate,
The high-mettled racer first starts for the plate,
The high-mettled racer first starts for the plate.

OH ! MOTHER A HOOP

OH ! MOTHER A HOOP

WHAT a fine thing I have seen to-day.
    Oh ! Mother a hoop !
I must have one, you cannot say nay,
    Oh ! Mother a hoop !
For husbands are gotten this way, to be sure,
Men's eyes and men's hearts they so neatly allure,
    Oh ! Mother a hoop !

OH! MOTHER A HOOP.—The words I have been unable to trace back from those given without reference in Chappell's book. The tune is given the same name in Wright's " Country Dances." This transcription of the tune is from Cibber's " Love in a Riddle," 1729. It was used in several ballad operas.

E

GRIMALDI'S LAST APPEARANCE

To face p. 49.

Nineteenth Century Songs

WHILE THE LADS OF THE VILLAGE

WE SHALL EITHER GET A GUINEA OR
A ONE-POUND NOTE

WHILE THE LADS OF THE VILLAGE

Charles Dibdin.   From " The Quaker," 1805.

WHILE the lads of the village shall merrily, ah !
      Sound the tabor, I'll hand thee along,
And I say unto thee that verily, ah !
      Thou and I shall be first in the throng.
      Thou and I shall be first in the throng.

Just then when the youth who last year won the dow'r
      With his mate shall the sports have begun,
When the gay voice of love is heard from each bow'r,
      And thou long'st in thy heart to make one.

While the lads of the village shall merrily, ah ! etc.

WE SHALL EITHER GET A GUINEA OR

A ONE-POUND NOTE

From " Don Giovanni."   T. Dibdin, J. Sanderson.

Sung by Lobsterina, Shrimperina and Don Giovanni
(Don Giovanni has fallen in the Thames.)

RAISE him up, raise him up,
      He fell out of yonder boat,
Get a cup, get a cup,
And pour it down his throat.
When he finds we took the trouble to keep his life afloat
We shall either get a guinea or a one-pound note.

L.   Pray you go just below, there's a little whiskey shop,
S.   You can tell very well where to get a little drop.
L.   Ma'am, in vain to send me hence,
      You would set your wits afloat,
      That you may get the guinea or the one-pound note.

D.G.   Who and where am I, and why thus upon the ground ?
L.   If you please, Sir, you be's a gentleman that's drowned.
D.G.   'Tis too plain in my brain, still yon boat the current stems.
S.   That's a hum for you come from the bottom of the Thames.
D.G.   And he that wouldn't leave it to meet a petticoat,
       Don't deserve a guinea or a one-pound note.

THE PLOUGHBOY

From THE POOR SAILOR ; or LITTLE BEN AND LITTLE BOB

THE PLOUGHBOY

By William Shields.   (1748-1829)   From " The Farmer."

A FLAXEN-HEADED cow-boy, as simple as may be,
   And next a merry plough-boy, I whistled on the lea,
Now a saucy footman I strut in worsted lace,
And soon I'll be a butler and wag my jolly face.
When steward I'm promoted I'll snip a tradesman's bill,
My master's coffers empty, my pockets for to fill ;
When lolling in my chariot so great a man I'll be,
So great a man, so great a man, so great a man I'll be,
You'll forget the little ploughboy that whistled on the lea.
You'll forget the little ploughboy that whistled on the lea.

I'll buy votes at Elections, but when I've made the pelf,
I'll stand poll for Parliament, and then vote in myself.
Whatever's good for me, Sir, I never will oppose,
When all my ayes are sold off, why then I'll sell my noes.
I'll joke, harangue and paragraph, with speeches charm the ear,
And when I'm tired in my legs, I'll just sit down a peer.
In Court or City honour, so great a man I'll be,
So great a man, so great a man, so great a man I'll be
You'll forget the little ploughboy that whistled on the lea,
You'll forget the little ploughboy that whistled on the lea.

From THE POOR SAILOR ; or LITTLE BEN AND LITTLE BOB

By Thomas Attwood.   Musical Drama in Two Acts.

MY William is the blythest youth
   That ever grac'd the Plain,
Of love, of constancy and truth
   I'll ne'er again complain ;
My flocks cou'd ne'er engage his sight,
   Too few, alas, were they,
In me alone he found delight,
   Then come my love away.

When dancing on the green each May
   He charms all hearts and eyes,
At cricket too I've seen him play,
   At cudgels win the prize.
With raptures each his merit tells,
   All tongues their tribute pay,
In ev'ry sport my swain excels ;
   Then come my love away.

A FROG HE WOULD A-WOOING GO.

A FROG he would a-wooing go,
    Heigho, said Rowley ;
A frog he would a-wooing go,
Whether his mother would let him or no,
With a rowley, powley, gammon and spinnage,
    Heigho ! said Anthony Rowley.

Off he set with his Opera Hat,
    Heigho ! said Rowley ;
Off he set with his Opera Hat,
On the road he met with a rat,
    With a rowley, etc.

They soon arrived at Mouses' Hall,
    Heigho ! said Rowley ;
They soon arrived at Mouses' Hall,
They gave a loud tap and they gave a loud call,
    With a rowley, etc.

Pray, Mrs. Mouse, are you within ?
    Heigho ! said Rowley ;
Pray, Mrs. Mouse, are you within ?
Yes, kind Sir, I'm sitting to spin—
    With a rowley, etc.

Come, Mrs. Mouse, now give us some beer,
    Heigho ! said Rowley ;
That Froggy and I may have some cheer,
    With a rowley, etc.

A FROG HE WOULD A-WOOING GO.

(Continued)

Pray, Mr. Frog, will you give us a song ?
    Heigho ! said Rowley ;
Let the subject be something that's not very long,
    With a rowley, etc.

Indeed, Mrs. Mouse, replied the Frog,
    Heigho ! said Rowley ;
A cold has made me as hoarse as a hog,
    With a rowley, etc.

Since you have caught cold, Mr. Frog, Mousey said,
    Heigho ! said Rowley ;
I'll sing you a song that I have just made,
    With a rowley, etc.

As they were in glee and merry-making,
    Heigho ! said Rowley ;
A Cat and her Kittens came tumbling in,
    With a rowley, etc.

The Cat she seized the Rat by the crown,
    Heigho ! said Rowley ;
The Kittens they pull'd the little Mouse down,
    With a rowley, etc.

This put Mr. Frog in a terrible fright,
    Heigho ! said Rowley ;
He took up his hat and he wish'd them good-night,
    With a rowley, etc.

As Froggy was crossing over a brook,
    Heigho ! said Rowley ;
A lily-white duck came and gobbled him up,
    With a rowley, etc.

So here is an end to one, two, and three,
    Heigho ! said Rowley ;
The Rat, the Mouse, and little Froggy,
    With a rowley, etc.

A FROG HE WOULD A-WOOING GO.—This song is included in Sam
Cowell's repertory. It is more or less traditional; a version of it is
in the " Pills to Purge Melancholy."

TIPPITIWITCHET

TIPPITIWITCHET

By William Reeve.

Sung by Grimaldi and later by Sam Cowell.

THIS morning early
　　My malady was such
I in my tea took brandy,
　　And took a drop too much.
Tol lol lol (hiccup)
Tol lol lol de rol de lay.

But stop ! I must not wag hard—
　　My head aches, if you please,
One pinch of Irish Blackguard
　　I'll take to give me ease.
Tol lol lol (sneezes)
Tol lol lol de rol de lay.

Now I'm quite drowsy growing,
　　For this very morn
I rose when cock was crowing,
　　Excuse me if I yawn.
Tol lol lol (yawns)
Tol lol lol de rol de lay.

I'm not in cue for frolic,
　　Can't my spirits keep,
Love, most melancholic,
　　'Tis that which makes me weep.
Tol lol lol (weeps)
Tol lol lol de rol de lay.

I'm not in mood for crying,
　　Care's a silly calf,
If to get fat you're trying
　　Then my way's to laugh.
Tol lol lol (laughs)
Tol lol lol de rol de lay.

TIPPITIWITCHET.—One of Grimaldi's most famous songs ; he sang it in Thomas Dibdin's " Bang up or Harlequin Prime," for which Reeve wrote the music. Reeve composed a great many songs, including a number of romantic ballads, his best known song being " A Friar of Orders Grey."

HOT CODLINGS

HOT CODLINGS

Sung by Grimaldi.

A LITTLE old woman her living she got
 By selling hot codlings hot, hot, hot :
And this little old women who codlings sold
Though her codlings were hot she felt herself cold,
So to keep herself warm she thought it no sin
To fetch for herself a quartern of—
Ri tol iddy iddy iddy, Ri tol iddy iddy ri tol lay.

This little old woman set off in a trot
To fetch her a quartern of hot ! hot ! hot !
She swallowed one glass and it was so nice,
She tipped off another in a trice :
The glass she filled till the bottle shrunk,
And this little old woman they say was—
Ri tol iddy iddy iddy, Ri tol iddy iddy ri tol lay.

This little old woman while muzzy she got
Some boys stole her codlings hot ! hot ! hot !
Powder into her pan put and in it round stones
Says the little old woman, " These apples have Bones."
The powder the pan in her face did send
Which sent the old woman on her latter——
Ri tol iddy iddy iddy, Ri tol iddy iddy ri tol lay.

The little old woman then up she got
All in a fury, hot ! hot ! hot !
Says she, " Such boys sure never were known
They never will let an old woman alone."
Now here is a moral, round let it buz,
If you mean to sell codlings never get ——
Ri tol iddy iddy iddy, Ri tol iddy iddy ri tol lay.

HOT CODLINGS.—The best remembered of Grimaldi's songs ; the music
is " arranged " by William Reeve. Grimaldi is said to have sung it at his
last appearance in public, 1828. Cruikshank drew an entrancing picture
of this for Dickens's memoirs of Grimaldi ; it shows Grimaldi sitting in
a chair (he was too ill to stand), taking snuff with a debonair gesture. The
snuff-box suggests that Cruikshank was remembering a performance of
Tippitiwitchet rather than this song.

SWEET KITTY CLOVER

SWEET KITTY CLOVER

Edmund Kean.   1837.   From the " Vocal Companion."

SWEET Kitty Clover, she bothers me so. Oh ! oh !
  Sweet Kitty Clover, she bothers me so.
    Her face is round and red and fat,
    Like pulpit cushion, or redder than that.
Oh, sweet Kitty Clover, she bothers me so. Oh ! oh !

Sweet Kitty in person is rather low. Oh ! oh !
    She's three feet tall and that I prize,
    As just a fit wife
    For a man of my size.
Oh, sweet Kitty Clover, you bother me so. Oh ! oh !

Where Kitty resides I'm sure to go. Oh ! oh !
    One moonlight night. Ah me ! What bliss !
    Through a hole in the window
    I gave her a kiss—
Oh, sweet Kitty Clover, you bother me so. Oh ! oh !

If Kitty to Kirk with me would go, Oh ! oh !
    I think I should never be wretched again,
    If, after the Parson,
    She'd say Amen !
Then Kitty would n'er again bother me so. Oh ! oh !

SWEET KITTY CLOVER.—I copied this from the " Vocal Companion "
for 1837 ; it is attributed to Edmund Kean. Can this have been the actor ?

POOR PUTTY

POOR PUTTY

Music by William Reeve.   Words by Chas. Dibdin, Junr.

Sung by Grimaldi.

WILL PUTTY was a glazier bold
    Whose head was of the putty mould,
He went a-courting to a scold
    Ri tol de rol tol de rol poor Putty !
To him she smooth as glass appears
But took him in all unawares,
For married soon she broke all squares.
    Tol de rol de rol tol tol,
        Tol de rol, Alas ! Poor Putty !

But glass is brittle, we all know,
And Billy soon he found it so,
For Mrs. Putty had a beau . . .
He found it out and words arise,
She broke his fanlights by surprise,
Which means she gave him two black eyes.
    Tol de rol de rol, etc.

This filled with pain the Glazier's head,
Who then resolved to be unwed,
And his dear Rib to Smithfield led . . .
For eighteenpence he sold her, list !
A parting kiss she would insist,
And picked his pocket while they kissed.
    Tol de rol de rol, etc.

The eighteenpence paid on the pin,
The Buyer hopped off with a grin,
Bill thought he'd took the Buyer in,
But Diamond here cut Diamond hard,
Bill missed his purse and then, poor lad,
He found the eighteenpence was bad.
    Tol de rol de rol, etc.

F

VILIKINS AND HIS DINAH

Con gusto and rather ritooralando.

VILIKINS AND HIS DINAH

IT is of a rich merchant I am going for to tell,
　Who had for a daughter an unkimmon nice gal,
Her name it was Dinah, just sixteen years old,
With a wery large fortune in silver and gold.
　　Ri-toorali, toorali toorali, da.

Now as Dinah was a-walkin' in the garding one day,
　　　　　(the front garding)
The father comed up to her and thus he did say,
Go, dress yourself, Dinah, in gorgus array
　　　　　(Take your hair out of papers)
And I'll bring you home a husband both galliant and gay.
　　　　Etc.

VILIKINS AND HIS DINAH.—Robson's most celebrated song.　He
introduced it at the Olympic Theatre, during Vestris and Planchet's manage-
ment, and later at the Grecian Saloon.　In the 'forties, Robson made famons
the pantomimes at the Grecian; he was pre-eminently an actor.　Vilikins
is a typical version of a traditional song persisting in a corrupted form.

GILES SCROGGINS

GILES SCROGGINS

GILES SCROGGINS courted Molly Brown,
 Fol lol de rol de rol de ra.
The fairest wench in all the town,
 Fol lol de rol de rol de ra.
She bought a ring with posy true,
" If you love me as I love you
No knife shall cut our loves in two."
 Tol lol de riddle lol de ra.

But scissors cut as well as knives,
 Fol lol de rol de rol de ra.
And quite uncertain is our lives,
 Fol lol de rol de rol de ra.
The day they were to have been wed
Fate's scissors cut poor Giles's head,
So they could not be married.
 Tol lol de riddle lol de ra.

Poor Mary laid her down to weep,
 Fol lol de rol de rol de ra.
And cried herself quite fast asleep,
 Fol lol de rol de rol de ra.
When standing all by the bed-post
A figure tall her sight engrossed,
And it cried, " I be Scroggins' ghost ! "
 Tol lol de riddle lol de ra.

The ghost it said all solemnly,
 Fol lol de rol de rol de ra.
" Oh Molly, you must go with I,
 Fol lol de rol de rol de ra.
All to the grave your love to cool."
Says she, " I am not dead, you fool."
Says the Ghost, says he, " Fie, that's no rule."
 Tol lol de riddle lol de ra.

The Ghost he seized her all so grim,
 Fol lol de rol de rol de ra.
And for to go along with him,
 Fol lol de rol de rol de ra.
" Come, come," said he, " e're morning beam."
" I won't," she cried, and gave a scream,
Then she woke and found she dreamed a dream,
 Tol lol de riddle lol de ra.

GILES SCROGGINS.—A clown song ; undoubtedly in Grimaldi's repertory.

BUBBLE AND SQUEAK AND PETTITOES

BUBBLE AND SQUEAK AND PETTITOES

C. Dibdin, Junr.

THERE was one Mr. Grigg,
  Wore a cauliflower wig,
And a-wooing he went with his set o' toes,
  To one Miss Sukey Snap,
  Who wore a high caul cap,
And was monstrously fond of pig's pettitoes.
  Week ! Week ! fol lol de ra.

In her favour to get
  He sent her a set,
And to ask him to sup with Miss Betty goes,
  And likewise to bespeak
  Some nice bubble and squeak,
For he loved that as well as she loved pettitoes.
  Week ! Week ! fol lol de ra.

E'er to sup they began
  Miss Betty for fun
Some sneezing powder to put in the pepper chose,
  Mr. Grigg was caught and sneezed,
  Saying Chih ! I hope you're pleased
With the Chih ! with the Chih ! with the pettitoes.
  Chih ! Chih ! fol lol de ra.

I vow, sir, says she,
  Nothing better can be
Than Chih ! Chih ! he ! he ! Betty goes.
  How's the bubble and squeak ?
  He for sneezing couldn't speak,
Till he sneezed off his wig among the pettitoes.
  Week ! Week ! fol lol de ra.

Sneezing, nodding went Miss Snap,
  Till the candle caught her cap,
And to put out the flame some water Betty throws,
  In vain, till Mr. Grigg,
  On the table dropped his wig
That was soaked in the gravy of the pettitoes.
  Week ! Week ! fol lol de ra.

Then poor Mr. Grigg
  Spoiled his cauliflower wig,
And Miss Snap lost her cap. What a set o' woes !
  For the house dog in the freak
  Boned the bubble and the squeak,
And Pussy ran away with the pettitoes (miaux !)
  Bow wow ! fol lol de ra.

OH ! MY LOVE'S DEAD

OH ! MY LOVE'S DEAD

Words by Charles Sloman.   Arranged by T. Westrop

Sung by Sam Cowell.

A S I vas a'valking along the sea-shore
Vere the loud vistling vinds and vater do roar,
Vith the sky for a kivering, the sand for the ground,
I heard a loud woice making sorrowful sound

    Crying Oh ! my love's dead whom I adore,
    So I never shall see my true Lovier no more.

She'd a woice like a sy-ringe and hair like a dove
And the song that she sang vas consarning of love,
She vas fairest of critters that ever vas seen,
Her shoes vas vite satin, her bonnet pea-green.

    Crying Oh ! my love's dead, etc.

I told her I'd jewels and diamonds in store,
Vith plenty of fine golden metal galore,
But she answer'd her hand to nobody she'd give
For she'd veep for her Villiam as long as she'd live.

    Crying Oh ! my love's dead, etc.

She look'd down on the vilds of the vide vatery vaste
And to pitch in head first she made very great haste,
Shouting out, now I'll dwell with the lobsters and crabs,
And live all my days with soles, mussels and dabs.

    Crying Oh ! my love's dead, etc.

KITTY OF THE CLYDE

KITTY OF THE CLYDE

Words by C. Dibdin, Junr.   Arranged by G. T. Westrop.

A BOAT danced on Clyde's bonny stream
　　When winds were rudely blowing,
There sat what might a goddess seem
　　O' the wave beneath her flowing,
　　O' the wave beneath her flowing.

But no, a mortal fair was she,
　　Surpassing a' beside,
And youth appeared her choice to be,
　　Sweet Kitty of the Clyde,
　　Sweet Kitty of the Clyde.

I saw the Boatman spread a sail,
　　And while his daftness noting,
The boat was upset by the gale ;
　　I saw Sweet Kitty floating,
　　I saw Sweet Kitty floating.

I plunged into the silver wave
　　With Cupid for my guide,
And thought my heart weel lost to save
　　Sweet Kitty of the Clyde.
　　Sweet Kitty of the Clyde.

But Kitty's aye a high born fair,
　　A lowly name I carry,
Ha' can in lordly Thames compare
　　Who woo the maid to marry ?
　　Who woo the maid to marry ?

But she na' scornful looks on me,
　　And joy may yet betide,
For hope now flatters, mine may be
　　Sweet Kitty of the Clyde,
　　Sweet Kitty of the Clyde.

OH ! CRUEL WERE MY PARIENTS

BUFFALO GALS

OH ! CRUEL WERE MY PARIENTS

Sung by all the Comic Singers.

OH ! cruel were my parients as tore my love from me,
  And cruel was the Press Gang as took him off to sea,
And cruel was the little boat as rowed him from the strand,
And cruel was the big ship as sailed him from the land.

> Sing too rol lol too rol lol lay.

Ah ! cruel was the water as bore her love from Mary,
And cruel was the fair wind as wouldn't blow contrary,
And cruel was the Captain, and the boatswain and the men
As didn't care a farden if we never met again.

> Sing too rol lol, etc.

CRUEL WERE MY PARIENTS.—A Burlesque on the traditional words
" Oh ! cruel was the Press Gang."

BUFFALO GALS

Sung by the Ethiopian Serenaders.

AS I was lumb'ring down de street, down de street, down de
    street,
A handsome girl I chanc'd to meet ;
  Oh, she was fair to view.

  Chorus :

> Buffalo gals, can't you come out to-night,
> Can't you come out to-night, can't you come out to-night ?
> Buffalo gals, can't you come out to-night ?
>   And dance by the light ob de Moon.

I ax'd her would she hab a dance, hab a dance, hab a dance,
I tought dat I might get a chance
  To shake a foot wid her.

  Chorus : Buffalo gals, etc.

I'd like to make dat gal my wife, gal my wife, gal my wife,
I'd be happy all my life
  If I had her by me.

  Chorus : Buffalo gals, etc.

MY LORD TOM NODDY

MY LORD TOM NODDY

M Y Lord Tom Noddy got up one day,
    And his Lordship rang for his cabriolet.
Tiger Tim was clean of limb,
His boots were polished, his jacket was trim.
With a very smart tie in his smart cravat
And a smart cockade on the top of his hat,
Tallest of boys and shortest of men,
He stood in his stockings just four foot ten.
And he asked, as he held the door on a swing,
" Pray did your Lordship please to ring ? "
" Yes, Tiger Tim, come, tell me true,
What may a nobleman find to do ? "

Tim bit his lip, Tim scratched his head,
Tim let go the handle, and thus Tim said,
As the door, releas'd, behind him banged,
" And it please you, my lord, there's a man to be hanged ! "
My Lord Tom Noddy jumped up at the news
And ran to Sir Carmaly Jenks of the Blues,
Took a squint at his watch, 'twas half-past two,
So he ran to McFuse and Lt. Tragoo.
" Rope-dancers a score I've seen before,
Mdme. Sacchi, Antonio and Master Blackmore ;
But to see a man swing at the end of a string,
With his neck in a noose, will be quite a new thing."

My Lord Tom Noddy stept into his cab,
'Twas dark rifle green with a lining of drab,
Thro' street, thro' square, his high trotting mare—
Like one of Ducrow's goes pawing the air.
Adown Piccadilly and Waterloo Place
Went the high-trotting mare at the deuce of a pace ;
She produced some alarm, but she didn't do harm
Save frighting a nurse with a child on her arm.
Knocking down, very much to the sweeper's dismay,
An old woman who wouldn't get out of the way,
Upsetting a stall, near Exeter Hall,
Which made all the pious Church mission folks squall.

DE BOATMEN'S DANCE

DE BOATMEN'S DANCE

Sung by the Ethiopian Serenaders.

DE Spring ob de year hab come at last,
Winter time is gwan and past,
Four-and-twenty Boatmen all of a flock,
Sitting on de seashore pecking off a rock ;

Chorus :
Dance de Boatmen dance,
O, dance the Boatmen dance ;
Dance all night 'till de broad daylight,
And go home wid de gals in de morning.
Hi ho, de Boatmen row,
Floating down de riber on de Ohio.

I went on board de oder day,
To hear what de Boatmen had to say ;
Dere I let my passion loose,
Dey cramm'd me in de calaboose.

Chorus : Dance de Boatmen dance, etc.

Oh, let me loose, I'll go ashore ;
Let me loose, I'll work no more ;
Stay now, nigger, dat'll neber do at all,
You've got to play to de Boatmen's ball.

Chorus : Dance de Boatmen dance, etc.

In come some wid bran new suits,
Long-tail'd coats and high-heel'd boots,
Get out ob de way, you hab no chance,
For dis is what dey call de Boatmen's dance.

Chorus : Dance de Boatmen's dance, etc.

NELLY BLY

TOBACCO

dolce.

NELLY BLY

Popular Negro Melody.

NELLY BLY, Nelly Bly, bring de broom along,
    We'll sweep de kitchen clean, my dear,
And hab a little song.
    Poke de wood, my lady lub,
An' make de fire burn,
    An' while I take de Banjo down
Jest gib de mush a turn.

Heigh ! Nelly, Ho ! Nelly, listen
    Lub to me,—
I'll sing for you, play for you,
    A dulcem melody.

NELLY BLY.—One of the " Negro " songs sung by the troupes which
followed in the wake of the Ethiopian Serenaders.

TOBACCO

TOBACCO is an Indian weed,
    Green, green in the morn, cut
Down at Eve.—
It shares our decay,
Man's life is but clay,
Think of this when you're
    Smoking Tobacco !

The pipe which is so lily-white,
In which so many take delight,
Is broken with a touch,
Man's life is but such,
Think of this when you're
    Smoking Tobacco !

The pipe that is so foul within
Doth show man's soul is stained with sin,
For then the Fire
It doth require.
Think of this when you're
    Smoking Tobacco !

The ashes which are left behind
They serve to put us all in mind
That unto dust
Return we must.
Think of this when you're
    Smoking Tobacco !

TOBACCO.—The authorship of " Tobacco " is assigned by Mr. John Blockley
to himself. It is, however, a much earlier song. John Blockley set a great
many of Tennyson's lyrics.

KEEMO-KIMO

KEEMO-KIMO

Sung by Sam Cowell.

IN South Carl'ina de darkies go,
  Sing-song Kitty, can't you ki-me-oh ?
Dat's whar de white folks plant de tow
  Sing-song Kitty, can't you ki-me-oh ?
Cover de ground all ober wid smoke
And up de darkies heads dey poke.

Chorus :

    Keemo-Kimo, dar ! Oh war ?
    Wid my hi, my ho, and in came Sally singing ;
    Sometimes penniwinkle, ling-tum rip-cat,
    Sing-song Kitty, can't you ki-me-oh ?

Milk in de dairy nine days old,
  Sing-song Kitty, can't you ki-me-oh ?
Frogs and mosquitos getting mighty bold,
  Sing-song Kitty, can't you ki-me-oh ?
Dey try for to slip, but it ain't no use,
Dere legs hang out for de chickens to roost.

    Chorus : Keemo-Kimo, etc.

Dere was a frog lived in a pool,
  Sing-song Kitty, can't you ke-mi-oh ?
And sure dis frog he was no fool,
  Sing-song Kitty, can't you ke-mi-oh ?
For he could dance and he could sing,
And make de woods all around him ring.

    Chorus : Keemo-Kimo, etc.

De widders' warm and so am I,
  Sing-song Kitty, can't you ki-me-oh ?
I'm sure you'd lub me if you'd try,
  Sing-song Kitty, can't you ki-me-oh ?
Your jet black face I lub to see,
Then put on your tucker and be off wid me.

    Chorus : Keemo-Kimo, etc.

KEEMO-KIMO !—Sung by Sam Cowell. One of many nonsense
introduced by the nigger troupes.

THE BALLAD OF SAM HALL

THE BALLAD OF SAM HALL

OH my name it is Sam Hall, it is Sam Hall,
  Oh, my name it is Sam Hall, it is Sam Hall,
My name it is Sam Hall, and I hate you one and all,
You're a gang of muckers all—
            Damn your eyes !

Oh, I killed a man, they said, so they said,
Oh, I killed a man, they said, so they said,
Oh, I killed a man, they said, for I hit him on the head,
And I left him there for dead—
            Damn his eyes !

Oh, they put me in the quad, in the quad,
Oh, they put me in the quad, in the quad,
Oh, they put me in the quad, and they tied me to a log,
And they left me there, by God—
            Damn their eyes !

Oh, the parson he did come, he did come,
Oh, the parson he did come, he did come,
Oh, the parson he did come, and he looked so mighty glum,
And he talked of Kingdom Come—
            Damn his eyes !

Oh, the Sheriff he came too, he came too,
Oh, the Sheriff he came too, he came too,
Oh, the Sheriff he came too, with his boys all dressed in blue.
There'll be bloody work to do,—
            Damn their eyes !

So up the rope I go, up I go,
So up the rope I go, up I go,
So up the rope I go, with my friends all down below,
Saying, '' Sam, we told you so ! ''
            Damn their eyes !

I saw Molly in the crowd, in the crowd,
I saw Molly in the crowd, in the crowd,
I saw Molly in the crowd, so I hollered right out loud,
'' Molly, ain't yer bloody proud ? ''
            Damn your eyes !

So this shall be my knell, be my knell,
So this shall be my knell, be my knell,
So this shall be my knell, and I'll meet you all in Hell,
And I hope you sizzle well—
            Damn your eyes !

SAM HALL.—In older versions the song referred to a certain Jack Hall.

CHEER ! BOYS, CHEER !

CHEER ! BOYS, CHEER !

(From " The Emigrant's Progress.")

Music by Henry Russell.   Words by Charles Mackay, LL.D.

CHEER ! boys, cheer ! no more of idle sorrow,
  Courage, true hearts, shall bear us on our way.
Hope points before—shows the bright to-morrow,
  Let us forget the darkness of to-day.
So farewell, England, much as we may love thee,
  We'll dry the tears that we have shed before,
Why should we weep to sail in search of Fortune ?
  So farewell, England, farewell for evermore !

Chorus :
  Cheer ! boys, cheer ! for Country, Mother Country ;
    Cheer ! boys, cheer ! the willing strong right hand ;
  Cheer ! boys, cheer ! there's wealth for honest labour ;
    Cheer ! boys, cheer ! for the new and happy land.

Cheer ! boys, cheer ! the steady breeze is blowing
  To float us freely o'er the ocean's breast,
The world shall follow in the track we're going,
  The stars of Empire glitter in the West.
HERE we had toil and little to reward it,
  But THERE shall plenty smile upon our pain,
And ours shall be the prairie and the forest
  And boundless meadows, ripe with golden grain.

Chorus: Cheer ! boys, cheer! etc.

CHEER! BOYS, CHEER!—Henry Russell introduced this song into one
of his musical entertainments. It is the most celebrated of the songs written
in collaboration with Charles Mackay, LL.D.   He is said to have sold it
outright for £5, and to have discovered afterwards that the publisher had
installed twenty-nine printing presses to meet the demands for the song.
The opening phrases of the tune remind one of the French folk-song " Joli
Tambour."

WOODMAN, SPARE THAT TREE

WOODMAN, SPARE THAT TREE

Music by Henry Russell.   Words by P. Morise.

WOODMAN, spare that tree !
   Touch not a single bough,
In Youth it sheltered me,
   And I'll protect it now.

'Twas my forefather's hand
   That placed it near his cot ;
There, Woodman, let it stand,
   Thy axe shall harm it not.

That old familiar tree
   Whose story and renown
Is spread o'er land and sea,
   Ah ! would'st thou hack it down ?

Woodman, forbear that stroke,
   Cut not its earthbound ties,
Oh ! spare that aged oak
   Now tow'ring to the skies.

When but a thoughtless child
   I sought its grateful shade,
With youthful sports beguiled
   Here, too, my sister played.

My mother kissed me here,
   My father pressed my hand ;
I ask, and with a tear,
   Oh ! let that old oak stand.

WOODMAN, SPARE THAT TREE.—Henry Russell was a singer as well as a very prolific writer of songs. He gave entertainments at the Hanover Square Rooms with his collaborator, Charles Mackay, in the 'forties. He lived to a great age and wrote his reminiscences.

THE OLD ARMCHAIR

THE OLD ARMCHAIR

Music by Henry Russell.   Words by Eliza Cook.

I LOVE it, I love it, and who shall dare
    To chide me for loving that old Armchair ?
I've treasured it long as a sainted prize,
I've bedewed it with tears, I've embalmed it with sighs.
'Tis bound by a thousand bands to my heart,
Not a tie will break, not a link will start.
Would ye learn the spell ? A Mother sat there,
And a sacred thing is that old Armchair.

In childhood's hour I lingered near
The Hallowed Seat, with listening ear,
And gentle words that Mother would give
To fit me to die—and teach me to live.
She told me shame would ne'er betide
With truth for my creed, and God for my guide,
She taught me to lisp my earliest prayer
As I knelt beside that old Armchair.

'Tis past, 'tis past, but I gaze on it now
With quivering breath and throbbing brow.
'Twas there she nursed me, 'twas there she died,
And Memory flows with Lava Tide.
Say it is folly, and deem me weak,
While the scalding tears drop down my cheek,
But I love it, I love it, and cannot tear
My Soul from my Mother's old Armchair.

THE OLD ARMCHAIR.—Eliza Cook specialised in piety, and wrote
a number of songs for Henry Russell. The engraving above this song shows
her standing by the armchair wearing a dressing-jacket ; she is holding
a pocket handkerchief. The window behind her is firmly shut.

THERE'S A GOOD TIME COMING

THERE'S A GOOD TIME COMING

Henry Russell.

THERE'S a good time coming, Boys, a good time coming,
　　We may not live to see the day,
But Earth shall glisten in the ray
　　Of the good time coming.
Cannon balls may aid the Truth,
　　But thought's a weapon stronger,
We'll win our battle of its aid,
　　Wait a little longer.

Chorus :

　There's　a good time coming, Boys, a good time coming,
　　Wait a little longer.

　There's a good time coming, Boys, a good time coming,
　War in all men's eyes shall be
　A monster of iniquity
　Nations shall not quarrel then
　　To prove which is the stronger,
　Nor slaughter men for Glory's sake,
　　Wait a little longer.

Chorus : There's a good time coming, etc.

　There's a good time coming, Boys, a good time coming,
　And a poor man's family
　Shall not be his misery
　　In the good time coming.
　Every child shall be a help
　　To make his right arm stronger,
　The happiest he, the more he has,
　　Wait a little longer.

Chorus : There's a good time coming, etc.

　　　Little children shall not toil
　　　Under or above the soil,
　　　　In the good time coming ;
　　　But shall play in healthful fields
　　　　Till limbs and minds grow stronger,
　　　And everyone shall read and write,
　　　　Wait a little longer.

Chorus : There's a good time coming, etc.

　　　The people shall be temperate
　　　And shall love instead of hate
　　　　In the good time coming.
　　　Smallest help, if rightly given,
　　　　Makes the impulse stronger,
　　　It will be strong enough one day,
　　　　Wait a little longer.

Chorus : There's a good time coming, etc.

WE MET

NOT FOR JOSEPH

CHORUS.

WE MET

From " Songs of the Boudoir," by Thomas Haynes Bayley.

WE met, 'twas in a crowd, and I thought he would shun me ;
He came, I could not breathe, for his eye was upon me ;
He spoke, his words were cold and his smile was unaltered,
I knew how much he felt, for his deep-toned voice faltered ;
I wore my bridal robe, and I rival'd its whiteness ;
Bright gems were in my hair, how I hated their brightness.
He called me by name as the bride of another,
Oh ! *thou* hast been the cause of this anguish, my Mother !

And once we met again—and a fair girl was near him,
He smiled and whispered low—as I once used to hear him,
She leant upon his arm—once, 'twas mine and mine only,
I wept, for I deserved to feel wretched and lonely ;
And she will be his Bride ! at the altar he'll give her
The love that was too pure for a heartless deceiver.
The world may think me gay, for my feelings I smother,
Oh ! *thou* hast been the cause of this anguish, my Mother !

NOT FOR JOSEPH

Written and composed by Arthur Lloyd.

JOSEPH BAXTER is my name,
My friends all call me Joe.
I'm up, you know, to every game,
And everything I know.
Ah, I was green as green could be,
I suffered for it though ;
Now, if they try it on with me,
I tell them not for Joe.

Chorus :
Not for Joe, not for Joe,
If he knows it, not for Joseph,
No, no, no,
Not for Joe.
Not for Joseph, Oh dear no !

H

I WISH HE WOULD DECIDE

I WISH HE WOULD DECIDE

By Haynes Bailey.   "Admired Ballad."

I wish he would decide, Mamma,
   I wish he would decide.
I've been a bridesmaid many times,—
   When shall I be a bride ?

My cousin Ann and sister Fan
   The nuptial knot have tied,
Yet come what will I'm single still,
Yet come what will I'm single still.
   I wish he would decide.
   When shall I be a bride ?
   When shall I be a bride ?

He takes me to the play, Mamma,
   And brings me pretty books ;
He woos me with his eye, Mamma,
   Such speechless things he looks.
Where'er I roam, abroad, at home,
   He lingers by my side.

Yet come what will I'm single still, etc.

I've thrown out many a hint, Mamma,
   I've spoke of other Beaux,
I've talked about domestic life,
   And sung, they don't propose.
Then if he means to break, Mamma,
   My passion and my pride
Unconquered yet, I'll scorn regret,
   Although he won't decide.

DISSOLVING VIEWS, or GOING, GOING, GONE

DISSOLVING VIEWS, or GOING, GOING, GONE

Words by Charles Slowman.   Arranged by T. Westropp.

I FREQUENTLY have puzzled been—
   Comparison to find
For Fortune's strange vagaries,
   Sometimes harsh and sometimes kind.
I think, at length, I one have found,
   Which I will state to you,
They nothing form, I certain am,
   But a '' grand dissolving view.''

Which is going, going, going,
   Till 'tis gone beyond recall,
For that we thought substantial
   Was a shadow on the wall.

The beauty of the Thames is gone,
   Of that there's not a doubt—
The silver stream is now all mud,
   And cannot be cleaned out.
The olden bridge of Westminster
   Is gone, for one that's new,
And vanished like a shadow
   Of the grand dissolving view.

Which is going, going, going, etc.

The King of Naples being gone
   In comp'ny with his Queen,—
The latter takes to shooting cats,
   A practice rather mean ;
Columbia North may fight the South,
   A course they both must rue ;
What pity 'tis their Union
   Is a grand dissolving view.

Which is going, going, going, etc.

The Drama, which in former days,
   Great talent could display,
Alas ! for want of mental strength
   Is fading fast away.
A Palace fair of industry
   We'll see in '62,
For that of '51 is gone
   Like a grand dissolving view.

Which is going, going, going, etc.

SLAP BANG, HERE WE ARE AGAIN!

SLAP BANG, HERE WE ARE AGAIN !

1866.

L ONG live our British Gentlemen
　　Who like a bit of sport,
Who smoke their weed and swig their stout
And won't have Gladstone's port !

Chorus :

　For they always go a-rolling home,
　They always go a-rolling home,
　　A jolly lot are they !
　　Tra la la, Tra la la.
　Slap bang, here we are again !
　Slap bang, here we are again !
　　A jolly lot are we !

　At cricket they can notch a few,
　　And tidily can box,
　But nothing say our swells unto
　　The torturing of cocks !

Chorus : For they always go a-rolling home, etc.

　When the Opera is out
　　And all the girls are home,
　Our swells light up the social pipe
　　And unto Evans' roam.

Chorus : For they always go a-rolling home, etc.

　And have a chop all piping hot,
　　Or pick a chicken wing,
　And take the odds upon the Oaks
　　The while the small boys sing.

Chorus : For they always go a-rolling home, etc.

　And get home with the morning milk
　　(The which of course is wrong,)
　And serenade the neighbourhood
　　With stanza for this song.

Chorus : For they always go a-rolling home, etc.

SLAP BANG, HERE WE ARE AGAIN !—The " Great " Alfred Vance's most celebrated song. Vance was George Leybourne's contemporary and rival. When Leybourne created " Champagne Charlie," Vance replied with a " Cliquot " song, and this led to a competitive series in praise of various brands of wine. Vance introduced the whiskered " masher " to the Halls ; he was versatile, however, and was famous for " Motto " songs such as " Act on the square, Boys, act on the square ! " He forestalled Chevalier with a coster song called " The Chickaleary Bloke."

BACON AND GREENS

BACON AND GREENS

Anonymous (in the '6o's).

I HAVE lived long enough to be rarely mistaken,
  And had my full share of Life's changeable scenes ;
But my woes have been solaced by good Greens and Bacon,
  And my joys have been doubled by Bacon and Greens.

What a thrill of remembrance e'en now they awaken
  Of childhood's young morning and youth's merry scenes—
One day we had Greens and a plateful of Bacon,
  The next we had Bacon and a plateful of Greens.

BACON AND GREENS.—Mr. Charles Coborn assures me that this was the
first of the food songs. It is anonymous, and was written in the 'sixties.
A verse of the song, not quoted, contains the couplet

  " Stick your fork in the fat, wrap your greens round the bacon,
    And you'll find there's no dish like good bacon and greens."

DARK TIMES CEASE FOR EVERMORE

DARK TIMES CEASE FOR EVERMORE

Anonymous, 1866.

L AY aside Religion's pleasures, and count its many tears
   While we all share sorrow with the poor,
There's a plaint sounding loudly forever in our ears—
  Oh ! Dark Times ! Cease for evermore.

    'Tis the wail, the sigh of the weary
    Dark Times, Dark Times come again no more !
    Dark Times come again no more !

Tho' in holiness and beauty we worship night and day,
   There are frail forms fainting at our door,
With a cry never silent and pleading looks we say
  Oh ! Dark Times ! Cease for evermore.

DARK TIMES CEASE FOR EVERMORE.—Number 1 of a series of
bridal songs for " the last days," " humbly dedicated in peculiar circumstances
to her most gracious Majesty Queen Victoria by her loyal and affectionate
subject the (anonymous) author," 1866.

The following explanation is made on the cover of the songs : " The
anonymous writer of these songs, after nearly half-a-century of unobtrusive
pastoral labour, was suddenly laid aside by paralysis, and medically
forbidden to read, converse, or even to think. Although he tried to obey, he
could not suspend the consciousness of a Christian man, and when the
time came that the 'bruised reed' might whisper, there burst forth two or
three songs such as the present one . . . first offered as an act of gratitude
for the return of cerebral power . . . during further convalescence . . .
he decided on presenting them as a humble contribution to the pious
necessities of the Age. At one time none could hope to possess the bijouæ of
pictorial art but the owner of a long rent-roll or a stately hall ; but now
everyone with the least pretensions to elegance can command them upon
the very china which adorns the toilette and the table. Why not something
of the same kind in music ? . . . Why not be helped to rise from the
domestic song with all the inspirations for good which are strong upon us
when we reverently hear out a sacred oratorio ? This, however unworthily,
is here attempted."

BOBBY BRUSH, THE BILL-POSTER

No doubt you wonder who I am,
   I am not any boaster,
But if you'd know, I am Bobby Brush,
   The world-wide known Bill Poster.
I paper all the stations round in
   Red, blue, green and yellow,
And tho' I sticks the people up—
   I am no stuck-up fellow.

Chorus :
   Brush, Brush, Brush,
      While all the world is hooking it,
   I brush, brush, brush.

I've heard some clever people say
   Truths stranger are than fictions,
And mine's a business in which you'll find
   Many contradictions——
I've posted '' Do you bruise your oats ''
   Because 'tis half the battle,
Next to a remedy for corns,
   And Thorley's food for cattle.

Chorus : Brush, Brush, Brush, etc.

BOBBY BRUSH, THE BILL-POSTER
(Continued)

I posts up the Christy Minstrels,
   'Cos I think they are the right boys,
Close to best Patent Blacking
   And the Drama of the White Boys.
Upon the wall I place Charles Kean,
   Of whom all men are praisors,
And just to prove I think him keen,
   I place him next to Mechi's Razors.

Chorus : Brush, Brush, Brush, etc.

I against the bricks placed Colleen Bawn
   At the Adelphi Quarter,
Next to a Bill that ask'd you
   If you'd take a turn by water.
An advertisement of Shakespeare offers
   An improved condition
And begs to say that Fechter takes
   The very next position.

Chorus : Brush, Brush, Brush, etc.

Charley Mathews, Mister German Reed,
   The famous Canterbury,
The Argyle Room, the Holborn,
   Stick up to make you merry.
To make me merry in your turn,
   And e'er I quit this station,
Just find me out a posting-place
   In your kind approbation.

Chorus :
   Then brush, brush, brush,
      But let me hear your plaudits
   While I brush, brush, brush.

CONTRARIETIES

CONTRARIETIES

MEN once were surnamed for their shape or their state,
(You all may from history worm it),
There was Lewis the Bulky and Henry the Great,
John Lackland and Peter the Hermit.
But now when the doorplates of misters and dames
Are read, each so constantly varies :
For the owners trade figure, and calling Surnames
All go by the rule of Contraries.

Mr. Box, tho' provoked, never doubles his fist,
Mr. Burns in his grate has no fuel ;
Mr. Playfair won't catch me at hazard or whist,
Mr. Coward got wing'd in a duel.

Mr. Drinkwater's apt to indulge in a dram,
Mr. Angel's an absolute fury,
And meek Mr. Lion let fierce Mr. Lamb
Break his nose in the lobby of Drury.

Mr. Barker's as mute as a fish in the sea,
Mr. Miles never moves on a journey,
Mr. Gotebed sits up till half after three,
Mr. Makepeace was bred an attorney.

Mr. Puny, whose father was rolling in wealth,
Knocked down all the fortune his Dad won,
Large Mr. Lefeuvre's the picture of health,
And Mr. Goodnight's but a bad one.

Mr. Crookshank stept into three hundred a year
By showing his leg to an heiress,
Now I'll hope you'll acknowledge I've made it quite clear
Surnames ever go by contraries.

LITTLE BILLEE AND GUZZLING JACK AND GORGING JIMMY,

or

There were three sailors of Bristol City,
They took a ship and went to sea.

W. M. Thackeray.   1867.

THERE were three sailors of Bristol city,
    They took a ship and went to sea,
They took a ship and went to sea.

There was Guzzling Jack and Gorging Jimmy,
    And a little boy they called Billee,
    And a little boy they called Billee.

And first they stuffed her with Captain's biscuits,
    And pickled pork, a large quantitee,
    And pickled pork, a large quantitee.

But soon they grew so precious greedy
    They had not got left one split pea,
    They had not got left one split pea.

To Guzzling Jack says Gorging Jimmy
    Oh, lawks, I feel so hungeree,
    Oh, lawks, I feel so hungeree.

And seeing as how we ain't got no wittles
    Why then, of course, we must eat we,
    Why then, of course, we must eat we.

Says Guzzling Jack to Gorging Jimmy :
    Oh ! what a precious fool you be,
    Oh ! what a precious fool you be.

LITTLE BILLEE AND GUZZLING JACK AND GORGING JIMMY,

or

There were three sailors of Bristol City,
They took a ship and went to sea.

(Continued)

There's little Billee there is young and tender,
    While we are old and tough, you see,
    While we are old and tough, you see.

Come, little Billee, we are going for to eat you,
    Undo the buzzom of your chi-mee,
    Undo the buzzom of your chi-mee.

Whilst Jim looked on and grinned assent,
    Bill pulled out his handkerchee,
    Bill pulled out his handkerchee.

Oh ! let me say my cat-er-chism,
    Which my old mother taught to me,
    Which my old mother taught to me.

Make haste, make haste, says Guzzling Jimmy,
    Whilst Jack pulled out his snippersnee,
    Whilst Jack pulled out his snippersnee.

And then little Bill ran to the top gallant mast,
    And kneeling down upon bended knee,
    And kneeling down upon bended knee.

He had not said his caterchism
    When, land, Oh ! land, I see, says he,
    When, land, Oh ! land, I see, says he.

I see Jerusalem and Madagascar,
    And North and South Americee,
    And North and South Americee.

And the British Fleet lying at anchor,
    And Admiral Napier, K.C.B.,
    And Admiral Napier, K.C.B.

And when they got to the Admiral's vessel,
    They flogged Jack, but they hanged Jimmee,
    They flogged Jack, but they hanged Jimmee.

And as for little Bill, they made him
    Captain of a seventy-three,
    Captain of a seventy-three.

[

MY HEART IS LIKE A SILENT LUTE

MY HEART IS LIKE A SILENT LUTE

Words by the Right Hon. B. Disraeli.   Music by G. F. Root.

MY heart is like a silent lute
  Some faithless hand has thrown aside,
Those chords are dumb, those tunes are mute,
  That once sent forth a voice of pride.
Yet even o'er the lute neglected
  The wind of Heaven will sometimes fly,
And even thus the heart dejected
  Will sometimes answer to a sigh,
And even thus the heart the heart dejected
  Will sometimes answer to a sigh.

And yet, to feel another's power
  May grasp the prize for which I pine,
And others now may pluck the flower
  I cherished for this heart of mine.
No more, no more, the hand forsaking
  The lute must fall, and shivered lie
In silence, and my heart thus breaking
  Responds not even to a sigh ;
In silence, and my heart thus breaking
  Responds not even to a sigh.

THE TWO OBADIAHS

THE TWO OBADIAHS

Words and Music by H. P. Lyste.

SAID the young Obadiah to the old Obadiah,
    I am dry, Obadiah, I am dry.
Said the old Obadiah to the young Obadiah,
    That's queer, Obadiah, so am I.
But the two Obadiahs had between them not a sou,
Every Publican smiled, and said, Oh ho ! my friend, it's you
May I ask, Obadiah, if you'll pay what is due ?
    Said the two Obadiahs, Oh be damned, Oh be damned !

Said the young Obadiah to the old Obadiah,
    I've a plan, Obadiah, I've a plan.
Said the old Obadiah to the young Obadiah,
    If that's so, Obadiah, I'm your man.
Said the young Obadiah, for weak liquor don't repine,
For my landlady's uncle sells a proper sort of wine,
It's in quarts, Obadiah, and it's called paraffine.
    Said the old Obadiah, that'll do, that'll do.

Said the young Obadiah to the old Obadiah,
    What a joke, Obadiah, what a joke !
Said the old Obadiah to the young Obadiah,
    Let us smoke, Obadiah, let us smoke.
But it's potent, Obadiah, and I feel I'm getting tight,
    Obadiah, Obadiah, Obaday.

Said the young Obadiah to the old Obadiah,
    I am drier, Obadiah, I am drier.
Said the old Obadiah to the young Obadiah,
    I'm on fire, Obadiah, I'm on fire !
As the two Obadiahs were consumed by their thirst,
The neighbours hurried in and prevented the worst,
By pumping so hard that the engines all burst.
    Obadiah, Obadiah didn't die !

    Moral :
        Said the old Obadiah to the young Obadiah,
            A lesson, Obadiah, I have learnt.
        Said the young Obadiah to the old Obadiah,
            I am burnt, Obadiah, I am burnt !
        And because, Obadiah, we did all but cremate,
        In future we will try to avoid such a fate.

        Oh ! smoking and drinking are sins very great
        Said the old Obadiah, stick to tea, stick to tea !

THE TWO OBADIAHS.—The most successful stunt song of the seventies.
The tune has been used later for " The bird on Nelly's hat."

CHAMPAGNE CHARLIE

Words and Music by Alfred Lee.   *Sung by George Leybourne.*

CHORUS.

I'VE seen a deal of gaiety
   Throughout my noisy life,
With all my grand accomplishments
   I never could get a wife.
The thing I most excel in is
   The P.R.F.G. game,
A noise all night, in bed all day,
   And swimming in Champagne.

Chorus :—
   For Champagne Charlie is my name,
   Champagne Charlie is my name,
   Good for any game at night, my boys,
   Good for any game at night, my boys.
   For Champagne Charlie is my name,
   Champagne Charlie is my name,
   Good for any game at night, my boys,
   Who'll come and join me in a spree ?

CHAMPAGNE CHARLIE
(Continued)

The way I gained my title's
 By a hobby which I've got
Of never letting others pay
 However long the shot ;
Whoever drinks at my expense
 Are treated all the same,
From Dukes and Lords, to cabmen down,
 I make them drink Champagne.

Chorus : For Champagne Charlie is my name, etc.

From Coffee and from Supper Rooms,
 From Poplar to Pall Mall,
The girls, on seeing me, exclaim
 " Oh, what a Champagne Swell ! "
The notion 'tis of everyone
 If 'twere not for my name,
And causing so much to be drunk,
 They'd never make Champagne.

Chorus : For Champagne Charlie is my name, etc.

Some epicures like Burgundy,
 Hock, Claret, and Moselle,
But Moet's vintage only
 Satisfies this Champagne swell.
What matter if to bed I go
 Dull head and muddled thick,
A bottle in the morning
 Sets me right then very quick.

Chorus : For Champagne Charlie is my name, etc.

Perhaps you fancy what I say
 Is nothing else but chaff,
And only done, like other songs
 To merely raise a laugh.
To prove that I am not in jest,
 Each man a bottle of Cham.
I'll stand fizz round, yes that I will,
 And stand it like a lamb.

Chorus : For Champagne Charlie is my name, etc.

CHAMPAGNE CHARLIE.—George Leybourne's best song. The majority of Leybourne's most successful songs were written by G. W. Hunt, but this song (by Alfred Lee) established his fame. He sang the song in whiskers and a gibus, holding a bottle in his hand. At some of his performances he stood free champagne to the entire audience.

THE GAY MASQUERADE

THE GAY MASQUERADE

By G. W. Hunt.

Sung by George Leybourne.

SOME like Garden-parties, some like Flower Shows
  For doing some spooning just " under the rose,"
Some are partial to concerts and lectures so staid,
But my weakness I fear is the Gay Masquerade.

Chorus :—

  I'm awfully fond of the Gay Masquerade,
  The light Masquerade, the bright Masquerade,
  With sweet pretty darlings in costume arrayed,
    The Gay Masquerade for me.

To say most daring things 'tis the easiest task
To some elegant Matron, whilst wearing a mask,
Oh ! the tales I have told and the vows I have made
There's no place for flirting like the Gay Masquerade.

Chorus :

  I'm awfully fond of the Gay Masquerade,
  The light Masquerade, the bright Masquerade,
  With sweet " Tootsy-Wootsys " so sweetly arrayed,
    The Gay Masquerade for me.

THE GAY MASQUERADE.—It was of Leybourne that George Edwardes
said that his personality would have been worth a thousand a week to him
in musical comedy. He died at an early age in the 'eighties, and was one of
the first four *lions comiques* known as great. He had great charm, and an
instinct for the theatrical value of clothes ; he started life as a bricklayer's
assistant.

I'LL STRIKE YOU WITH A FEATHER

I'LL STRIKE YOU WITH A FEATHER

By Arthur Lloyd.

Sung by G. H. Macdermott.

I'LL sing of Hildebrand Montrose
　　(His proper name is Charlie),
He speaks as tho' with a " cold id his dose,"
　　Bad French he tries to " parley."
His hair is in Barber's ringlets,
　　His eyes are made up dark,
He walks upon his uppers
　　While strolling in the park.

Chorus :

Au revoir, ta ta ! you'll hear him say
To the Marchioness Clerkenwell while bidding her good day,
I'll strike you with a feather, I'll stab you with a rose,
For the darling of the ladies is Hildebrand Montrose.

His scarf, unlike himself, is green,
　　His gloves, " no kid," are " yaller,"
His washed-out pants are well-strapp'd down,
　　He carries a " fake " umbrella ;
He never pays his tradesmen,
　　To him they'll give no trust,
He drinks dry Champagne " cider "
　　Until he's fit to " bust."

Chorus : Au revoir, ta ta ! etc.

His " stock in trade " of socks count three,
　　He chalks his paper collars,
He always pays his taxes
　　For his income's just two dollars ;
He swears he'll wed a " Duchess "
　　Tho' he waits till " all is blue,"
Tho' he goes to bed a beggar
　　Wakes up " the Lord knows who."

Chorus : Au revoir, ta ta ! etc.

I'LL STRIKE YOU WITH A FEATHER.—This was written by the
comic singer, the " great " Arthur Lloyd, and later sung by the equally famous
G. H. Macdermott. Although written in the 'seventies, it suggests a fierce
campaign against Wilde's aesthetic movement.

COVENT GARDEN IN THE MORNING

COVENT GARDEN IN THE MORNING

Music by R. Coote.   Words by J. L. Graydon.

Sung by George Leybourne.

IT'S now after dark, I'm out for a lark,
 The pleasure I seek is not harming ;
With a lad for a mate which will suit first rate,
 The effect I am sure will be charming.
To a place we'll go, our paces to show,
 When the first break of day is dawning,
Away with our mates to cool our pates,
 We'll off to Covent Garden in the morning.

Cherries so red, strawberries ripe ;
 At home, of course, they'll be storming,
Never mind the abuse, you have the excuse
 You went to Covent Garden in the morning.

COVENT GARDEN IN THE MORNING.—A vehicle for George Leybourne's particular type of " charm." Oscar Wilde also discovered the fascination of Covent Garden early in the morning, but people don't seem to go there now.

MY GRANDFATHER'S CLOCK

MY ANGEL MOTHER DEAR

MY GRANDFATHER'S CLOCK

Words and Music by Henry C. Work

(A Christy Minstrel song).

MY Grandfather's clock was too large for the shelf,
  So it stood ninety years upon the floor ;
It was taller by half than the old man himself,
  Though it weighed not a penny-weight more.

It was bought on the morn of the day that he was born,
  And was always his treasure and pride ;
But it stopped short, never to go again,
  When the old man died.

MY ANGEL MOTHER DEAR

Words by George Calvert.   Music by Richard Percy.

THERE is a soft, a holy name
  Round which the feelings close
In globe-like forms, that mock to shame
  The fire that passion knows ;
Whate'er my fate—where'er I rove,
  That name is ever near,
Oh ! 'tis the bliss of life to love
  My Angel Mother Dear.

The mind recalls the waning eve
  When round her bed we hung,
And our fond hearts could not believe
  The shadow death had flung.
Between eternity and time
  I see a last low ray
Waiting to bear her, rob'd, sublime,
  Up to the realms of day.

THE TIME IS COMING

By G. W. Hunt.

SOME say I'm seeking place,
    And on ambition I am busy,
Because I speak plain English
    Like Palmerston and "Dizzy";
I care not who may steer the ship,
    Nor who may be the crew,
But when I see there are rocks ahead
    I speak out, so should you!

Chorus :
    Oh, the time is coming and it won't be long,
    The sooner the better as we're all gone wrong,
    What with plundering at home and blundering abroad,
    There'll have to be a change ere long.

THE TIME IS COMING

(Continued)

The Boers our Flag treat with insult,
And as for Zululand !
It is a glorious muddle which
No man can understand.
Whilst Gladstone's busy chopping trees,
And Granville gently sleeps,
The Russian Bear t'wards India
Nearer and nearer creeps.

Chorus : Oh, the time is coming, etc.

They worked you up a Franchise Bill
And speeches they outpoured ;
It was but dust to blind your eyes
From looking out abroad.
I say, by all means give the Vote
If it betters the Constitution,
But you have to thank the Tories
For the new Redistribution.

Chorus : Oh, the time is coming, etc.

And as for the wretch " Rossa " !
Mr. Gladstone set him free,
In '69, to work his fiendish
Plot across the sea :
In his dynamatic villainy,
Yet no steps did they take
To call upon America
To " scotch " the foulest snake.

Chorus : Oh, the time is coming, etc.

We've lost brave men, and bold Burnaby
Who died with sword in hand ;
A true Briton, a true soldier,
Worthy hero of our land !
And as for gallant Gordon
They left him to his fate
Until, to save disgrace, they sent
Relief, yes ! when too late !

Chorus : Oh, the time is coming, etc.

Too late has been their motto,
Too late they've proved, but strange
If Englishmen don't think it's not
Too late to have a change.
The time will not be long ere's heard
The knell that tolls the doom
Of this blundering, perhaps 'twill happen
When the primrose is in bloom.

Chorus : Oh, the time is coming, etc.

K

NIX MY DOLLY PALS

NIX MY DOLLY PALS

G. H. Rodwell.

IN a box of the stone jug I was born,
　Of a hempen widow the kid forlorn,
　　Fake away.
My noble father as I've heard say
Was a famous merchant of capers gay.
　　Nix my Dolly Pals fake away,
　　Nix my Dolly Pals fake away.

The knucks in quod did my shoolmen play
And put me up to the time of day,
No dummy hunter had fakes so fly, (¹)
No knuckler so deftly could fake a cly (²)
　　Nix my Dolly Pals fake away, etc.

But my nuttiest lady one fine day
To the beaks did her gentleman betray,
And thus was I bowled out at last
And into the jug for a lag was cast.
　　Nix my Dolly Pals fake away, etc.

But I slipped my darbies one morn in May
And gave to the dubsmen a holiday,
And here I am, Pals, merry and free,
A regular rollicking Romany.
　　Nix my Dolly Pals fake away, etc.

(¹) Thief.　　　　(²) To pick a pocket.

NIX MY DOLLY PALS.—The words of this song were introduced from Harrison Ainsworth's "Rookwood" into Rodwell's Comic Opera, "Little Jack Shepherd."

KISSING ON THE SLY

THE GRECIAN BEND

KISSING ON THE SLY

Music by G. H. Marden.   Words by H. Watkins.

H IS manly whiskers swept her cheek,
  She uttered no reply—
How could she part her lips to speak
  While kissing on the sly ?
There such a sum of smacking bliss,
  That Crœsus could not buy
The honey'd worth of one sweet kiss
  That's taken on the sly.

Oh, this kissing on the sly,
This kissing on the sly,
  This wooing winning style of sinning,
Kissing on the sly !

THE GRECIAN BEND

Music by Alfred Lee.   Written by Ben Walker, Esq.

I 'M glad to see you, one and all,
  And hope I don't intrude,
In such a fashionable style
  No one can think me rude.

Absurdities in any form
  I'm anxious to amend,
And so I've introduced a style
  I call the " Grecian Bend."

Chorus :
  Oh, the latest style is the " Grecian Bend,"
  It's all the " go " you may depend,
  It makes your hair all stand on end
  To see girls doing the " Grecian Bend."

OH, WHAT A FORWARD YOUNG MAN YOU ARE

OH, WHAT A FORWARD YOUNG MAN YOU ARE

By John Read.   About 1880.

Sung by Beatrice Bermond.

SOME young men when courting are awfully shy,
    And when you speak to them will scarcely reply,
While some are so forward, you cannot deny
    They make a girl look like a fool.
And that's just the way with my cousin Joe,
Whenever I meet him I'd have you to know
That he will insist upon stealing a kiss,
    Then I unto him have to say

Chorus :

    Oh Joe ! do let me go,
    Let me alone or I'll tell Mamma.
    Oh Joe ! do let me go,
    Oh ! what a forward young man you are.

One night at a party, just for a lark,
He turned out the gas, left us all in the dark ;
The ladies they screamed and each gent did remark,
    What a foolish young man to be sure.
When the gas it was lit all eyes were on me,
The ladies they tittered, and each young man he
Commenced then to laugh, so I said there must be
    With me something wrong I am sure.
I ran to the glass at a terrible pace,
And saw the print of his moustache on my face,
Which, of course, had been dyed, Oh what a disgrace,
    And enough to make a young girl say—

    Chorus : Oh Joe ! etc.

I was just about making my way from the place,
When I felt Joseph's arms encircle my waist,
And the warm pressure of his lips to my face
    And once again I had to say—

    Chorus : Oh Joe ! etc.

DON'T GO OUT TO-NIGHT, DEAR FATHER

DON'T GO OUT TO-NIGHT, DEAR FATHER

Music by W. L. Thompson.   Words by M. E. Golding.

DON'T go out to-night, dear father,
  Don't refuse this once, I pray ;
Tell your comrades mother's dying,
  Soon her soul will pass away ;
Tell them, too, of darling Willie,
  Him we all so much do love,
How his little form is drooping
  Soon to bloom again above.

Chorus :
  Don't go out to-night, dear father ;
    Think, oh think how sad 'twill be
  When the angels come to take her,
    Papa won't be there to see.

Tell me that you love dear mamma,
  Lying in that cold, cold room,
That you don't love your comrades better,
  Cursing there in that saloon.
Oh, dear father, do not leave us,
  Think, oh think, how sad 'twill be,
When the angels come to take her,
  Papa won't be there to see.

Chorus : Don't go out to-night, etc.

Morning found the little pleader
  Cold and helpless on the floor,
Lying where he madly struck her
  On that chilly night before ;
Lying there, with hands uplifted,
  Feebly uttering words of prayer ;
Heavenly Father, please forgive him,
  Reunite us all up there.

Chorus : Don't go out to-night, etc.

PLEASE SELL NO MORE DRINK TO MY FATHER

PLEASE SELL NO MORE DRINK TO MY FATHER

Words by Mrs. F. B. Pratt.   Music by C. A. White.

PLEASE, Sir, will you listen a moment,
    I've something important to say,
My mother has sent you a message,
    Receive it in kindness, I pray.
'Tis of father, poor father, I'm speaking,
    You know him, he's called Ragged Gore ;
But we love him, and hope we may save him,
    If you'll promise to sell him no more.

Chorus :

Please sell no more drink to my father,
    It makes him so strange and so wild,
Heed the prayer of my heart-broken mother,
    And pity the poor drunkard's child.

My father came home yester even,
    Reeled home thro' the mud and the rain ;
He upset the lamp on the table,
    And struck my sick mother again.
Then all of the hours till the morning
    He lay on the cold kitchen floor,
And this morning he's sick and he's sorry,
    Oh ! promise to sell him no more.

Chorus : Please sell no more drink to my father, etc.

When sober, he loves us so dearly,
    No father is kinder than he ;
He wishes so much to stop drinking,
    But this is the trouble you see :
He cannot withstand the temptation
    He feels when he passes your door
As he goes to his work in the morning,
    PLEASE promise to sell him no more.

Chorus : Please sell no more drink to my father, etc.

TRUE FRIENDS OF THE POOR

TRUE FRIENDS OF THE POOR

A Philanthropic Song dedicated to The Philanthropic Societies of Great Britain, by T. S. Lonsdale, the author.

N OW give me a man,
 Who has proved he's a man,
No matter his rank or his birth—
In life's path there's weeds,
Not many good deeds
By which you may know a man's worth.
He may wear a crown,
A bright silken gown,
And never want gold, you are sure ;
But still you will find
He thinks of mankind,
And never turns one from his door.

Chorus :

And such a man as that was Lord Shaftesbury
Whose name and fame will live for evermore,
A good and noble man was Lord Shaftesbury,
An honest and a true friend to the poor.

A man like a friend
His hand will extend
And help a poor brother in need,
Without hope of gain,
To me it is plain
He's really a true friend indeed.
He don't want applause,
For by Nature's laws
We all should do good when we can,
And with a good heart
Each should play his part
And help, if he can, a poor man.

Chorus : And such a man as that was Mr. Montefiore, etc.

Chorus : And such a man as that was Mr. Peabody, etc.

TOMMY, MAKE ROOM FOR YOUR UNCLE

Words and Music by T. S. Lonsdale.

FRED JONES, Hatter, of Leicester Square,
　　Presents himself to you,
And you may guess when he is dressed
　　Of girls he knows a few ;
A Widow fell in love with him,
　　While riding in a train,
She had a spoiled boy with her,
　　Who caused us both much pain.

TOMMY, MAKE ROOM FOR YOUR UNCLE
(Continued)

Chorus :
    Tommy, make room for your Uncle,
        There's a little dear !
    Tommy, make room for your Uncle,
        I want him to sit here.
    You know Mamma has got a bun,
        And that she'll give it you,
    So don't annoy, there's a good boy,
        Make room for your Uncle, do.

Spoken: Yes, the confounded young urchin caused me a great deal of pain and sorrow; and the Widow, his Mother, introduced me to him as his Uncle! Fred Jones was never an Uncle before, and never will be again, not if he knows it—and the whole of the journey the Mother said to the boy:

Chorus : Tommy, make room for your Uncle, etc.

When first I met the firm of Green,
    'Twas on my journey down
To spend a day at Rosherville,
    " Just like a swell from Town."
The Widow loved romantic scenes,
    And a squeeze on the sly,
But when my arm went round her waist
    The boy began to cry !

Spoken: Yes, it would never do to make love before the boy, and the widow said "Not before the boy, Fred, not before the boy." Just then we went under a tunnel and she said :

Chorus : Tommy, make room for your Uncle, etc.

The Mother told her loving son
    To watch the passing train,
But " No," he said, " my Uncle Fred
    Will kiss your hand again."
The Widow blushed a maiden blush,
    And I was not myself,
For who can make love on a seat
    In front of that young Elf ?

In a sunny retreat at Rosherville
    I went down on my knees,
And asked if she would fly with me
    Across the bright blue seas ?
She sighed and said, " You wicked man,
    But how about the child ? "
And clasped him fondly to her breast,
    While I the agony piled !

Spoken: I said, "My lovely of all lovely beings, let us fly to some foreign clime—where I will protect you and your boy." She answered and said, "How about my little Pie Shop in Seven Dials?" "Oh, Bloomsbury, do you keep a Pie Shop?"

Chorus : Tommy, make room for your Uncle, etc.

THE CITY TOFF,
or
THE CRUTCH AND TOOTHPICK

CHORUS.

THE CITY TOFF,

or

THE CRUTCH AND TOOTHPICK

Words by E. V. Page.   Music by Vincent Davies.

L ET me introduce a fellah ! Lardy dah ! Lardy dah !
  A fellah who's a swell ah ! Lardy dah ! Lardy dah !
Tho' limited his screw, yet the week he struggles thro' it,
For he knows the way to do it, Lardy dah ! Lardy dah !
For he knows the way to do it, Lardy dah ! Lardy dah !

Oh, he often dines for fourpence. Lardy dah ! Lardy dah !
When he hasn't any more pence. Lardy dah ! Lardy dah !
And then the artful fellah
Picks his teeth like any swell ah !
Just outside the Grand Hotel, ah ! Lardy dah ! Lardy dah !
Just outside the Grand Hotel, ah ! Lardy dah ! Lardy dah !

Chorus :
    And he wears a penny flower in his coat. Lardy dah !
    And a penny paper collar round his throat. Lardy dah !
        In his hand a penny stick,
        In his mouth a penny pick,
    And a penny in his pocket. Lardy dah !

THE CITY TOFF.—E. V. Page was a schoolmaster who took to writing
lyrics. This song was one of Nelly Power's greatest successes. Male costume
had not yet been popularised by Vesta Tilley, and she sang the song in tights
and spangles.

L

SHE DOES THE FANDANGO ALL OVER THE PLACE

Words and Music by G. W. Hunt.

I 'VE seen many beauties
　　Whilst travelling around
The world, but in Spain
　　There my fancy I found ;
She'd hair black as coal,
　　Eyes bright as a star,
And I fairly felt gone
　　As she twanged her guitar !

Chorus :

　　She sang like a nightingale, twanged her guitar ;
　　Danced the Cachuca, smoked a cigar ;
　　Oh ! what a form ! Oh ! what a face !
　　And she did the Fandango, all over the place.

　　Spoken: On being introduced to her father, a villainous-looking personage,
he said something like this—"Hah! Sistenato! Allegretto! Cigaretto!" I
said, "My dear Sir, you are quite right in your observation." There was
something wrong somewhere, for he flourished a dagger, and said: "Ho!
Delapo! Bodega! Intimidado!"—and so to soothe him—

SHE DOES THE FANDANGO ALL OVER THE PLACE

(Continued)

To England I brought her
To make her my bride,
And when my friends saw her
They laughed till they cried,
And the buttons flew off
From a dozen white vests
When at breakfast she somewhat
Astonished the guests.

Chorus : She sang like a nightingale, etc.

But she carries her Spanish ways
Slightly too far,
I, at times, think she'll have
To destroy her guitar ;
For she sits at the window
And sings long and loud,
Until in the streets
She collects a large crowd.

Spoken : And horrid boys cry out, "Chuck it out, Sarah !" Dreadful !
And when I insist on her concluding her performance she rushes into the
garden, mounts the Summer House, and won't come down till she's—

Sung like a nightingale, twanged her guitar ;
Danced the Cachuca, smoked a cigar ;
Dev'lish bad form, quite a disgrace,
She WILL do the Fandango all over the place.

SHE DOES THE FANDANGO ALL OVER THE PLACE.—This song
was, of course, inspired by the vogue for foreign dances such as the " Can Can."
G. W. Hunt was a prolific writer of songs for comedians.   He also wrote the
famous patriotic song " We don't want to fight, but by Jingo ! if we do."

THE NEW ELECTRIC LIGHT

CHORUS.

Moon - light, lime - light, and the light of day,

Sil- ber light and can-dle-light, are not half so bright, Gas - light, Bude-light,

soon will pass a - way; All must take a back seat thro' e - lec- tric light.

THE NEW ELECTRIC LIGHT

Words by F. W. Green.   Music by Alfred Lees.

OH, have you heard the latest news
  Of how the world's to be
Soon lighted up from pole to pole
  With electricity ?
The light of day will be eclipsed
  Soon by the light of night,
When all the Earth's illuminated
  By electric light.

Chorus :

  Moonlight, limelight, and the light of day,
    Silber light and candle-light,
      Are not half so bright ;
  Gaslight, bude light soon will pass away,
  All must take a back seat thro' electric light.

'Twill show up the atrocities committed in the East,
And throw a light on Russia's shifty policy at least ;
And in the House of Parliament we shall learn aright
The policy of Beaconsfield by the new electric light.

DEAR OLD PALS

CHORUS.

DEAR OLD PALS

By G. W. Hunt.

Sung by G. H. Macdermott.

I LIKE my share of pleasure,
  And I'll have it if I can ;
I love a loving woman,
  And respect an honest man.
I like to find true friendship
  In the life that's rolling by,
And such is always found between
  My old pal Tom and I.

Chorus :
  We're dear old pals, jolly old pals,
    Clinging together in all sorts of weather,
  Dear old pals, jolly old pals,
    Give me the friendship of dear old pals.

We've tasted of the ups of life,
  We've also felt its " downs " ;
Sometimes our pocket held bright gold
  And sometimes only " browns " ;
And be our drink bright, sparkling " cham,"
  Or merely humble beer,
The grasp of friendship's been the same
  Through each succeeding year.

Chorus : We're dear old pals, etc.

We do snug little dinners,
  And they pass off very nice,
I put my old pal on the chair,
  He makes me take the vice :
We toast her gracious Majesty,
  We don't forget the " gals " ;
But *the* toast of the evening is
  Success to true old Pals !

Chorus : We're dear old pals, etc.